WELCOME
TO THE NIGHT SKY

Since 2006, I have written a monthly guide for *Sky at Night Magazine* to help beginners get to grips with many aspects of the night sky. The idea is to make stargazing as accessible as possible, from helping you to learn the constellations to the practicalities of how to use a telescope. In providing this knowledge of the night sky, the intention has always been to keep jargon down to a minimum so the basics can be understood with ease.

Now, for the first time, we're bringing these guides together into one 'manual'. If you're curious about astronomy, this guide has everything you need to know to get off to the best possible start. The contents have naturally fallen into three areas: in 'Need to know' we'll help you understand the sizes, distances and basic nature of the skies; in 'What to use' we cover the equipment you can use to study the night; and in 'What to see' we'll look at the objects and events that are waiting for you in the night skies above, such as eclipses, double stars and the Milky Way.

It's amazing how much we've covered, and it just shows what an incredible and varied subject astronomy is. We hope you find the *Beginners' Guide to Astronomy* useful as your stargazing quest begins.

Anton

Anton Vamplew

ABOUT ANTON

Astronomy writer Anton Vamplew has appeared regularly on TV and radio to give his accessible insight into observing the night sky, including on *Blue Peter* and across the BBC World Service. His popular first book has been updated: *New Simple Stargazing* is now available on the iPad.

CONTENTS

IMMEDIATE MEDIA℃ᴼ

The *Beginners' Guide to Astronomy* is published by Immediate Media Company Bristol Limited under licence from BBC Worldwide.

EDITORIAL
Editor Chris Bramley
Writer Anton Vamplew
Production Kev Lochun, Russell Deeks, Rob Banino

ART AND PICTURES
Art Director Michelle Mclaren
Design Steve Marsh, Lynne Guyler, Sheu Ho
Picture Research Steve Marsh, Sarah Kennett

ADVERTISING SALES
Advertising Director Caroline Herbert
Advertisement Manager Steve Grigg 0117 314 8365
Inserts Laurence Robertson 00 353 87 690 2208

PRODUCTION
Production Manager Emma McGuinness
Production Director Sarah Powell
Ad Services Manager Mel Watkins
Ad Co-ordinator Fred Bennett
Ad Designer Nathaniel Brain
Reprographics Tony Hunt, Chris Sutch

LICENSING
Head of Licensing and Syndication Joanna Marshall

MARKETING
Head of Circulation Rob Brock
Head of Marketing Marie Davies
Marketing Co-ordinator Georgina Pearson
Head of Press and PR Carolyn Wray 0117 314 8812

PUBLISHING
Publisher Andrew Davies
Managing Director Andy Marshall

MANAGEMENT
Chairman Stephen Alexander
Deputy Chairman Peter Phippen
CEO Tom Bureau

BBC WORLDWIDE MAGAZINES UNIT
Managing Director Nicholas Brett
Publishing Director James Hewes
Editorial Director Jenny Potter
Unit Co-ordinator Eva Abramik

EDITORIAL ADVISORY BOARD Nicholas Brett, Tom Bureau, Deborah Cohen, Jane Fletcher, James Hewes, John Lynch, Jenny Potter, Kathy Sykes

SUBSCRIPTION RATES FOR SKY AT NIGHT MAGAZINE
Annual subscription rates (inc P&P): UK cheque/credit card £57; Europe & Eire Airmail £69; rest of world airmail £79. To order, call 0844 844 0260

© Immediate Media Company Bristol Limited 2012
ISBN 0563531876

recycle
When you have finished with
this magazine please recycle it.

IN THIS MAGAZINE

> NEED TO KNOW
• Get started with naked-eye observing
• Astronomy terms explained

So, you've found a nice dark spot in the northern hemisphere for your first night of stargazing, but where do you begin?

Here's where – it's called the Plough, and it's a recognisable pattern made up of seven bright stars. In UK skies, it never goes below the horizon

THE FIRST NIGHT

START STARGAZING THE RIGHT WAY

When you start thinking about astronomy, your mind can end up anywhere – you could speculate about life in the Universe, future human missions to Mars, or the creation of gold in a supernova explosion (that's the cataclysmic ending event for a star much larger than the Sun).

Maybe you'd simply like to find your way around the night sky, or possibly your enquiry is more philosophical, such as: what's it all about? Now that last one remains a mystery, but the point just before about getting to know the stars is much easier to tackle.

For newer stargazers, it's possible that the best starry views you have encountered so far were when you were on holiday. I certainly know that Mediterranean skies, for example, seem that much darker, with the stars shining brighter than at home. There's also an issue here that when you're on holiday, you're more relaxed and therefore have more time to gaze skyward, so that's actually a good time to get to know the night sky.

THE BRIGHTEST STARS

Back home, many of us live in a town or city with much light pollution, which does indeed give the sky an orange wash. In fact, I learnt the night sky from a fairly polluted area. Strangely, this can help: here the fainter stars are not visible, which leaves only the brightest and best of the bunch, which tend to be the ones that outline the constellations.

Once, not long after I'd first started stargazing, I was visiting La Palma, in the Canary Islands off northwest Africa, where the skies are amazingly dark and clear. This sounds ideal, but in fact it took me an agonisingly long time to find anything because all those annoying fainter stars had become visible and ruined the patterns I understood. Moral: light pollution, although not good, is no bad thing for learning the sky.

So, where do you actually start if you find yourself with a clear night? All the stars in every direction we look in have been grouped into areas known as constellations. There are actually 88 in total, but some are easier to see and indeed form 'signposts' that can be used to find many others in different parts of the sky.

The place to begin if you live in the mid-to-high latitude northern hemisphere, which includes the UK, is a group of seven stars known as the Plough (or the Big Dipper in the USA). The reason for telling you about the hemisphere is that you'll find that these fairly bright Plough stars never go below the horizon. Hence you will always be able to see this group if it is a clear night, no matter what time of year it is.

KNOW WHERE NORTH IS

To locate the Plough, you just need a knowledge of where north is from where you are looking. Simply speaking, that is off to the left of where the Sun

JARGON BUSTER

• CONSTELLATION An area of the night sky, the brightest stars of which sometimes form recognisable patterns.

• NORTHERN HEMISPHERE The half of the Earth from around the equator 'up' to the North Pole.

• STAR A glowing ball of gas that makes its light and heat by nuclear reactions. Stars can be of different sizes depending on how much gas they are made of.

• UNIVERSE Everything we know is the Universe: this includes all the stars, galaxies, dust, gas, planets, comets – the whole lot – plus energy, space itself, and what we know as time.

❯ WHAT TO USE
- Choosing telescopes and binoculars
- Mounts, eyepieces and filters
- Get started in astrophotography

❯ WHAT TO SEE
- Observing the Sun, Moon and planets
- Double stars, clusters and the Milky Way
- Nebulae and other deep-sky objects

GETTING USED TO THE DARK

In order to see the stars properly you need to take into account a very important factor to do with your eyes. This is called dark adaptation

You'll notice your pupils are larger in dark conditions to let in more light, and smaller on a bright sunny day so as not to dazzle you. This is actually only a small part of what your eyes are up to.

Basically, eyes adapt to whatever the lighting conditions are. Let's take an example: a room at night with the lights on. It all looks fine because your eyes have set themselves to work in whatever light there is around. Now turn the lights off and the first thing you'll notice is that the room appears almost black for a short time. Your eyes, sensing the lack of light, have gone into dark-adapting mode – your pupils grow to let in more light and then the all-important chemical changes

Pupils are smaller in bright conditions so that the light does not dazzle

In the dark, your pupils grow bigger to let in more light – vital for seeing the stars

begin to switch on the low-light-intensity 'rods' which fill the backs of the eyes, so you can see more. This process actually takes around an hour, but a good proportion is complete within 10 minutes or so.

In other words, to see the best of the faint night sky, shield your eyes from bright lights for a good few minutes before you start stargazing. Plus, make sure you cannot see any bright lights while you are observing.

This isn't the view that someone spinning on the spot at night would see – it's a picture taken over an hour to show how much the stars move at night

rises, or to the right of where the Sun sets. The highest the Sun gets in any day is due south, so of course north is opposite to this. Alternatively, you can always use a compass!

Now we have to contend with the rotating and moving Earth. Just as the Sun rises, moves over the sky and sets, so many of the stars do the same thing at night – though not all. Some stars stay up all night long, including the Plough. As the Earth

itself moves around the Sun we also see a slight shifting of stars night-by-night, which means some constellations enter and leave our skies over the course of a year.

Once again, the Plough is always there 365 days a year, due to its location and our location on Earth. Which all leads to it being a most handy pattern to learn, and from which to launch your stargazing quest and get to know the starry skies.

WHAT NEXT Notice how the Plough appears to move over the course of just a few hours – a consequence of the Earth's rotation.

DISCOVER THE UNIVERSE

Try 3 issues for just £5*
when you subscribe by Direct Debit!

If you have enjoyed the *Beginners' Guide to Astronomy* and want to learn more about the Universe, why not try *Sky at Night Magazine*? With in-depth features on the latest areas of cosmological research, *Sky at Night Magazine* is your practical guide to astronomy, featuring star charts, observing tutorials and in-depth equipment reviews. Whatever your level of knowledge, you'll find something to enjoy in the night sky.

Your special subscription offer

➤ **3 issues for just £5***
➤ Continue to **save 25%** after your trial period
➤ **Exclusive CD-ROM** with every issue
➤ Receive **free UK delivery** direct to your door

✍ SUBSCRIBE ONLINE
www.buysubscriptions.com/skyatnight
☎ CALL US ON 0844 844 0254†

NEED TO KNOW

UNDERSTAND THE VIEW OF THE NIGHT SKY WE GET FROM PLANET EARTH

The sky at night is one of the most alluring sights, inviting observers to imagine what is happening out there far away around a distant star, or to ponder the chances of life existing elsewhere in the cosmos.

Thanks to centuries of scientific

We begin with the stars and how these points of light are described by fellow astronomers, why they sometimes shimmer and how to use the constellations they're organised into as signposts to find your way around.

We also introduce a way of looking

WHERE STARS ARE BORN

The Orion Nebula is a fine example of a stellar nursery, for here it is estimated that around 1,000 stars are being made at this moment. Different parts of the cloud, which is made up mainly of dust and hydrogen gas, are beginning to pull themselves together under gravity. As more gas piles in, the temperature in the centre of a clump rises. If there's enough gas and a temperature of 10 million °C is reached, then nuclear reactions will start and a star will be born.

OBSERVING STARS

WHY SOME STARS LOOK MUCH BRIGHTER THAN OTHERS AND WHY THEY APPEAR TO TWINKLE

Occasionally the night sky just sparkles, and it's a terrific sight. When there's been a rain shower or something has cleared the air of all the dust, the stars look really amazing.

Nights like these can be truly memorable, and reveal the full beauty and majesty of the Universe, or rather, a small part of it. At such times we seem to see loads of stars and the best ones stand out even more than usual. This effect can even happen in a built-up area where, with this clearer air, the streetlights do not have so much to illuminate and so there is less light pollution.

One thing is instantly apparent, and that is the brightness of the stars. There are a few that are very bright, some medium ones and heaps of fainter stars that are more difficult to discern.

NASA/ESA/M. ROBBERTO (SPACE TELESCOPE SCIENCE INSTITUTE/ESA) AND THE HUBBLE SPACE TELESCOPE ORION TREASURY PROJECT TEAM

STAR PERFORMERS

The brightest stars visible from the northern hemisphere

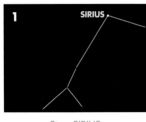

Star: SIRIUS
Magnitude: −1.5
Constellation: Canis Major

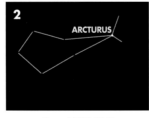

Star: ARCTURUS
Magnitude: 0.0
Constellation: Boötes

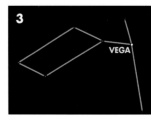

Star: VEGA
Magnitude: variable 0.0
Constellation: Lyra

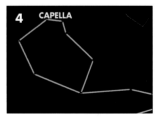

Star: CAPELLA
Magnitude: +0.1
Constellation: Auriga

Sirius, the Dog Star, is the brightest star in the night sky, making it easy to recognise

How bright a star looks is called its 'apparent visual magnitude'. You may see this written as 'apparent magnitude', 'visual magnitude' or just 'magnitude'. You may also see it abbreviated to 'mag.', as we do throughout the *Beginners' Guide to Astronomy*.

What's strange about magnitude scales is that the numbering system is back to front – the brighter the star, the lower the number it is given. So a star of mag. +2.0 is therefore brighter than one that's mag. +5.0. To understand why this is, we have to cast our minds back more than 2,000 years and think about how the ancient Greeks tried to make sense of the heavens.

STARING INTO SPACE

If you could travel back to ancient Greece, the best person to seek out would be an astronomer and mathematician called Hipparchus. His initial thoughts about the night sky were probably the same as yours: it's immediately clear that not all of the stars and other astronomical objects are the same brightness.

Hipparchus called this varying in brightness 'magnitude' and based on this he catalogued the stars into six groups. The 20 brightest stars were labelled magnitude 1, or the 'first magnitude'. Slightly fainter stars fell into magnitude 2, and so on. Hipparchus continued down to magnitude 6, which were the faintest stars he could see with his eyes.

Today, we use scientific equipment to classify magnitude exactly, and we use it to measure the brightness of all objects in the sky – not just the ones visible to the naked eye, and not just stars. But Hipparchus's structure remains. Our modern system is, of course, much more accurate, with the mathematical difference between one magnitude and the next being about 2.5 times the brightness. This means that a first magnitude star is 2.5 times brighter than a second magnitude star, and so on, right up to around 100 times brighter than a 6th-magnitude star.

However, the scale doesn't bottom out at one. To make things even more interesting, a star can have a magnitude of zero, which would be a pretty bright star; objects that are brighter still are given a minus number. For example, the planet Venus, when at its brightest, appears at mag. –4.7. This is why positive magnitudes are marked with a '+' sign, to remove any ambiguity.

Sliding back down the scale – getting fainter – we return to mag. +6.0. This is typically the limit of what you can see with the naked eye; anything dimmer and it's likely that you'll need a pair of binoculars or a telescope to see it. In actuality, this depends on your eyes: some people have no trouble seeing down to mag. +6.5 or lower.

So, what about the stars we know and love? Well, the brightest star in the night sky is Sirius, the leading star in the constellation of Canis Major, the Great Dog. Its visual magnitude is a dazzling –1.5. Compare that with Polaris, the North Star,

MORE ADVICE OVER THE PAGE

WHY DO STARS TWINKLE?

Twinkle, twinkle, little star, how I wonder what you are... Well, we don't mean to disappoint any children who might be reading this, but actually it's not the star twinkling at all.

The light from the star may have travelled for many millions of years though space – nice and steadily, all the way – and then it meets Earth's atmosphere, which is where all the twinkling takes place.

Here the light is reflected, bent, shimmered and shaken by all the tiny bits that make up our atmosphere, until it makes it to your eye. Stars would not appear to twinkle if we viewed them from outer space, or from a planet or moon that didn't have an atmosphere.

Light from a distant star

Earth's atmosphere

Stars 'twinkle' because we view their light through turbulent air

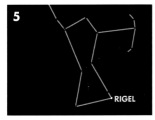

Star: RIGEL
Magnitude: +0.1
Constellation: Orion

Star: PROCYON
Magnitude: +0.4
Constellation: Canis Minor

Star: ACHERNAR
Magnitude: +0.5
Constellation: Eridanus

Star: BETELGEUSE
Magnitude: variable +0.6
Constellation: Orion

TOP TEN
BRIGHTEST OBJECTS

1 **THE SUN**
Magnitude: –26.7
As seen from Earth

2 **THE MOON**
Magnitude: –12.6
At full Moon

3 **VENUS**
Magnitude: –4.7
At its brightest

4 **MARS**
Magnitude: –2.9
At its brightest

5 **JUPITER**
Magnitude: –2.9
At its brightest

6 **MERCURY**
Magnitude: –1.9
At its brightest

7 **SIRIUS**
Magnitude: –1.5
Northern hemisphere star
Brightest star in the night sky

8 **CANOPUS**
Magnitude: –0.7
Southern hemisphere star,
second brightest in the
night sky

9 **SATURN**
Magnitude: –0.3
At its brightest

10 **ALPHA CENTAURI**
Magnitude: –0.3
Leading star in the
southern hemisphere
constellation of Centaurus

OTHER OBJECTS

**FAINTEST STARS IN A
LIGHT-POLLUTED URBAN SKY**
Magnitude: +3.0

**FAINTEST STARS VISIBLE FROM
A DARK-SKY SITE**
Magnitude: +6.5

**FAINTEST STARS VISIBLE WITH
10x50 BINOCULARS**
Magnitude: +9.5

**FAINTEST STARS VISIBLE WITH
THE HUBBLE SPACE TELESCOPE**
Magnitude: +30.0

CAUTION
DO NOT LOOK
AT THE SUN WITH
THE NAKED EYE OR
ANY UNFILTERED
MAGNIFICATION
DEVICE

Although the Sun is the brightest
star in our skies, in absolute terms
it's dimmer than Rigel in Orion

The Moon is the brightest
object in the night sky
when in a full phase

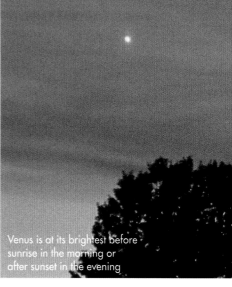

Venus is at its brightest before
sunrise in the morning or
after sunset in the evening

Mars is easily distinguished by it ruddy hue, giving rise to the nickname 'the Red Planet'

Jupiter may not be the brightest planet in the Solar System, but it's certainly the largest

JUDGING MAGNITUDES

Looking up at the sky, sometimes people say that a star is really big. Of course this isn't the case, as all stars are so far away that they only ever appear as points of light to your eye. It's what your eye does with that dot that can make it seem bigger. And, in fact, drawing bigger dots is the only way of showing the difference in star brightness on a chart. The brighter stars have the biggest dots. There will generally be a key to the dots and what magnitude they represent nearby. It's a good idea to get acquainted with the faintest stars you can see in your usual night sky. Take a star chart and look for the smallest dots (the faintest stars) in a recognisable constellation and see if they're visible in the sky. Then you'll know how much your viewing is affected by light pollution.

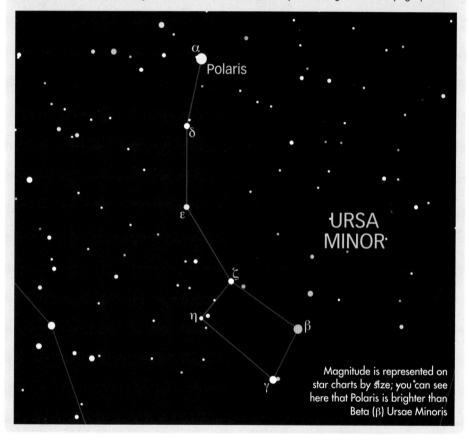

URSA MINOR

Magnitude is represented on star charts by size; you can see here that Polaris is brighter than Beta (β) Ursae Minoris

in the constellation of Ursa Minor – its magnitude is just +2.0. With practice, it is possible for the eye to spot differences of one-tenth of a magnitude between stars – now there's something to try of an evening.

Of course, stars are at different distances from Earth, and come in many sizes and colours. So visual magnitude only tells us how the brightness of one differs from another in the sky. It tells us nothing about a star's 'absolute brightness'.

What do we mean by absolute brightness? Well, if you lined all the stars up at the same distance from Earth, you would be able to truly see how bright each star is. It's just like being in a field during a pretty bad party – there are only a few people dotted around and no-one is talking to each other. Wherever you stand, you aren't able to judge who is the tallest. However, if you rounded everyone

up and made them stand in a line 5m in front of you, you would easily be able to tell.

Of course, 5m away is not going to work with a star! Astronomers use a distance of 32.6 lightyears. A star's magnitude, as viewed from this calculated distance, is its 'absolute magnitude'. But how do you move a star 32.6 lightyears away? Not with some strange gravity device, I can assure you.

To get the absolute magnitude for each star we just need to know its visual magnitude (easy: it's in a book) and how far away it is (easy again: space telescopes have worked that one out for us).

We know that brightness diminishes with distance, just as a bonfire doesn't appear to be as bright if you look at it from a distant hill as it does if you are standing next to it. If we know the distance to a star and how bright it looks from here, then we can work out its absolute magnitude.

WHAT NEXT

It's a really worthwhile getting to know the faintest stars you can see from where you live – in other words, the limiting visual magnitude of the skies above you. Try this on a few occasions, as you may find the seeing conditions are different each time. Any good constellation guide will give you the visual magnitude of stars right down to mag. +6.0, so out you go. You'll have fun and may just learn something into the bargain. Just don't forget your red torch.

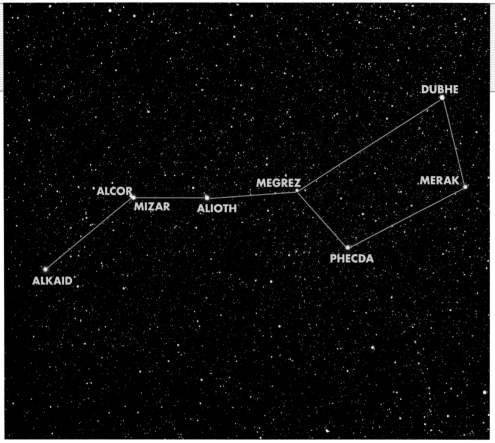

JARGON BUSTER

• ASTERISM A pattern of bright stars that can be easily found again and again. Famous asterisms include the Plough, the Summer Triangle and Orion's Belt.

• DOUBLE STAR Two stars that appear very close together. They may actually be orbiting each other, in which case they are known as a binary double, or they can simply appear to be close because of our viewpoint in space, in which case they are known as an optical double.

• STAR COLOURS Stars can be different colours depending on the amount of gas they are made of and how far through their lives they are.

Get to know the stars that make up the Plough: Alkaid, the Alcor-Mizar double, Alioth, Megrez, Dubhe, Phecda and Merak. In case you're wondering, these stars all owe their names to medieval Arabic astronomers

SIGNPOSTS IN THE STARS

USE THE PLOUGH AND OTHER STARRY SHAPES TO FIND YOUR WAY AROUND THE NIGHT SKY

FINDING YOUR WAY FROM THE PLOUGH

The Plough doesn't just help you to find Polaris. Here are four more stars, and their constellations, that the Plough will point you towards

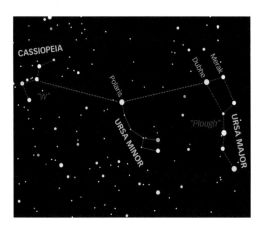

❯ CASSIOPEIA
You've already seen how to locate Polaris. Now continue this imaginary line onwards for the same distance that you've already come from the Plough, take a slight bend to the right, and you arrive at the constellation of Cassiopeia, the Queen, which appears in the form of a W-shaped group of stars.

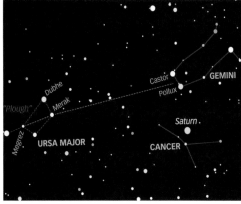

❯ CASTOR AND POLLUX, THE TWINS OF GEMINI
To get to Castor and nearby Pollux, the main stars of Gemini, the Twins, start from the Plough star Megrez. Head for Merak, diagonally opposite it, and keep going. Almost halfway to your target you'll pass the two stars that form the front paws of Ursa Major.

RED TORCHES

You're observing; your eyes are dark-adapted, and yet you'd still like to see charts and be sure that you're not about to step on a hedgehog. The answer is a torch adapted with red paper, red cellophane sweet wrappers or red paint over the front. Dark-adapted eyes are much less sensitive to red light. Just make sure the red light is not too bright, as that will ruin your dark adaption: all you need is enough light to see by. You can also buy purpose-made red light torches, so no DIY is required.

On page 6, we introduced our first group of stars, the Plough, and mentioned how useful it was for finding the other stars and constellations around the starry skies. Indeed, you could call the Plough a signpost to the stars.

However, before we actually cast off and stargaze further afield, there are a few things to look at in the Plough itself.

Firstly, it's worth noting that each of the Plough's seven stars has its own name. Notice where the star Mizar is – it's located right at the 'bend' in the Plough's handle. This star, together with a companion that's not quite as bright, forms a well-known double star that is visible to the unaided eye. Apparently, at some stage it was used to test whether you had good eyesight, although how reliable that test really could have been is debatable, as Mizar's companion is not a very faint star, and you can see it quite easily.

So what exactly are you looking for? Well, with the Plough in its usual orientation as a saucepan sitting flat on a cooker, take a look to the top-left of Mizar at a distance of about one-third of the diameter of the Moon – that's about one-third of the width of your little finger.

There, with any luck, will be Mizar's companion: a star named Alcor. This is the first of many double stars that we'll find.

BELONGING TO THE BEAR

Both Mizar and its companion Alcor are white stars, but on the other side of the Plough is our first coloured star. The top-right star of the main 'saucepan' part has a slight orangey-yellow hue. This star is called Dubhe. It is the brightest star in the Plough, and indeed it is also the leading star of the constellation to which the Plough belongs.

Just to clear up any confusion at this point, the Plough is not a constellation: technically, it is what's called an asterism. This simply means that it is a group of stars that are easily recognisable. The actual constellation to which the Plough belongs is Ursa Major, the Great Bear. Our saucepan friend creates the back and tail of the Bear.

Many constellations look nothing like the animal, person or object they are supposed to represent, but Ursa Major is actually one of the exceptions. Mind you, you still need a fair amount of imagination! So next time you're out, have a go at the joining the dots on the Great Bear.

Anyway, back to Dubhe. The best way of seeing its orangey-yellow hue is to compare it with the star below it in the Plough: the pure white Merak. If you flip your sight between these two, then the orangey-yellow colour of Dubhe should be apparent.

POINTING THE WAY

Now that you know where Dubhe and Merak are, you've just met two of the most useful stars in the night sky. These two stars are known as the Pointers, because they can be extremely useful when it comes to locating other stars.

Starting with Merak, draw an imaginary line through Dubhe and keep going. The next star of any note you come across is the very famous Polaris (also known as the Pole Star) or North Star. Don't expect this to be a super-bright example of stellar marvellousness – it isn't. Polaris is just an ordinary-looking star. It's famous because it sits almost directly above Earth's North Pole, so as we spin, this star appears to stay practically in the same place.

And that's just the start – the Plough can help you find many more stars and constellations.

HOPPING WITH BINOCULARS

Binoculars provide another way to star-hop. The trouble is, when you look through them it's easy to lose your bearings because you're only looking at a small piece of sky. So it's useful to work out how much of the sky your binoculars show you (their field of view).

To do this, take a look at the Plough, noting which stars are at the very edge of the view through your binoculars. Now find these stars on a star chart and make a ring out of wire and place it around them. This ring is the field of view of your binoculars at the right scale to use on your star chart.

You can then move your wire ring around the chart to plan each step of your star-hop and know what the view should look like. Try aiming for the Double Cluster in Perseus – it's a great target through binoculars, and lies close to Cassiopeia.

REGULUS AND LEO
To get to Leo, the Lion, you also start from Megrez, but this time trace a line through Phecda, below it in the Plough. Continuing on this line you travel to Regulus, the leading star in Leo. The head of the Lion is made by an easily seen sickle-shaped asterism of stars that works up from Regulus.

CAPELLA AND AURIGA
To find Auriga, the Charioteer, start again from Megrez, but this time take a route through Dubhe, to its right. After an expanse of emptiness that includes the very faint constellation of Camelopardalis, the Giraffe, you will eventually arrive at the bright yellow star Capella, the lead star of Auriga.

TURN THE PAGE FOR MORE TARGETS

❯ TARGET 1: M31

M31, the Andromeda Galaxy, is one of the most distant objects you can see with your own eyes from a dark location. This is an unaided-eye route, but trying it with binoculars shows the difference that increased magnification makes. The best time to attempt this is in the autumn, when it gets dark early.

So in mid-October at 9pm, this six-stop hop starts at Alpheratz, the top-left star in the Great Square of Pegasus asterism (**1**). Move to the next star to the left, Delta (δ) Andromedae (**2**). Now move left again, but slightly higher, to Beta (β) Andromedae (**3**). The next hop is to the star directly above, Mu (μ) Andromedae (**4**), and then directly above that again, to the star Nu (ν) Andromedae (**5**). A few finger-widths diagonally right of this is the smudge of M31 (**6**).

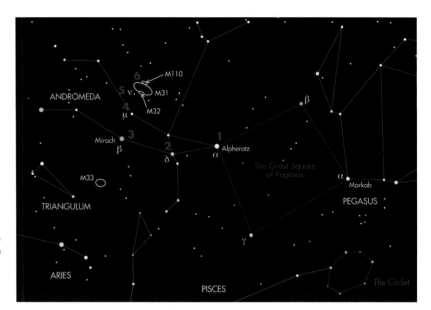

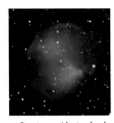

❯ TARGET 2: M27

Next, we're going to use binoculars to hop in five steps from the Summer Triangle asterism, which in mid-October is high in the southwest at 9pm, to M27, the Dumbbell Nebula.

Begin at Altair, the lowest star of the Summer Triangle (**1**). Look a short distance (about 10°) upwards from Altair and you will come across the small, five-star constellation Sagitta, named for its appearance as an arrow. From the left-most star in Sagitta, Eta (η) Sagittae (**2**), follow a chain of fainter, mag. +6 and +7 stars northwest (**3**) until you arrive at mag. +5.5 14 Vulpeculae (**4**). You may well have found M27 already – it's to the lower left of this star (**5**).

Note that at other times of the year, the starhopping directions will shift somewhat, because of the rotation of the Earth.

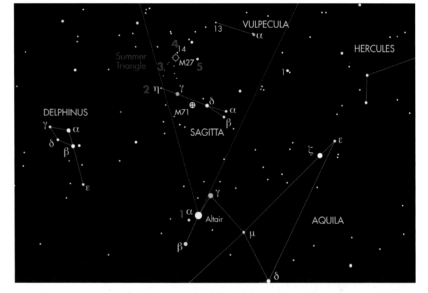

❯ TARGET 3: M11

The Wild Duck Cluster, M11, is a fine object in binoculars – and it will look even better through a telescope. Getting there, however, needs nothing more than a four-stop hop that you can navigate with the naked eye.

Once again, start from the Summer Triangle's southernmost star, Altair (**1**), at 9pm in mid-October. Move your gaze down and right 15° to Delta (δ) Aquilae (**2**), then down the same amount again, but not so much to the right, until you get to Lambda (λ) Aquilae (**3**). Now hop down to Eta (η) Scuti (**4**), the right-most of the two fainter stars that you'll see trailing off to the right of Lambda. Train your binoculars just below the mid-point between this star and Beta (β) Scuti to the right (**5**), and there is M11 (**6**).

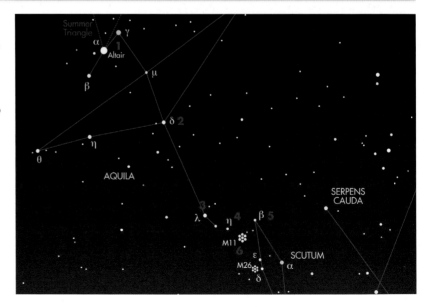

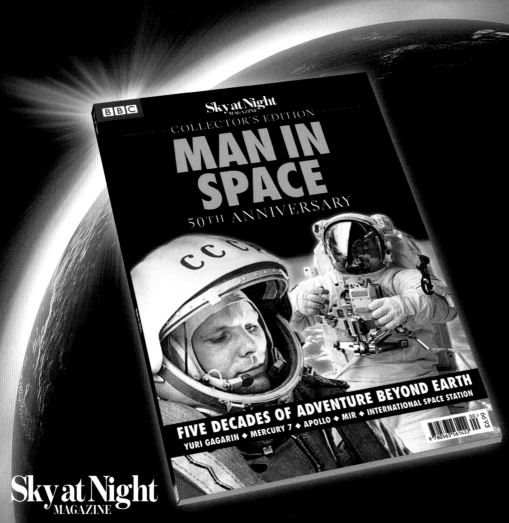

STAR CO-ORDINATES

HOW ASTRONOMERS DESCRIBE THE POSITION OF ANY GIVEN OBJECT IN THE NIGHT SKY, SO THAT YOU KNOW WHERE TO LOOK FOR IT

USING CHARTS

If you're looking for the star Deneb on a chart, you can find it with the following coordinates:

Right ascension (RA)
20h 41m 25.9s

Declination (Dec.)
+45° 16' 49"

Clearly, this is not all just nice simple degrees. In declination the ' symbol represents angular (or arc) minutes and the " represents angular (or arc) seconds.

A degree is a pretty large unit on the sky – two widths of the full Moon, in fact! So, 1° is divided into 60 arcminutes and each arcminute has 60 arcseconds – used for super accuracy or very small things. The + or – at the start shows whether it is in the northern (+) or southern hemisphere (–).

Right ascension is written as hours, minutes and seconds – as in regular time, not the arcseconds of declination. This is why, for example, minutes are shown as m (time variety) and not ' (arc variety). So, one hour in RA describes the movement of the sky due to Earth's spin over an hour – which is 15°, because 15° x 24 (hours) is 360°, and that's all the way round over the course of a day.

Yes, it's bonkers! Needless to say, star charts are all divided up nicely, so there's no need to convert anything – just plot the position and there will be Deneb, in the tail of Cygnus, the Swan.

On page 29, we'll be looking at the brain-defying units of length in space, and how astronomers work out just how far apart things like galaxies or stars really are. But you can forget all about that for now. It's all truly fascinating stuff and great for discussions with a cup of tea over the garden fence, but there's no practical benefit in knowing that Deneb is over 70 times further away than Vega when you're out with your telescope.

The fact is, everything is so far away from us that we can consider it to be the same distance. This applies as much to a distant galaxy billions of lightyears away as it does to the Moon at just a few hundred thousand kilometres. Include man-made satellites and you bring the figure down to a few hundred kilometres.

What is the point of assuming everything's at one distance? It allows us to describe the position of something, as well as locate that celestial wonder. This is all done by the power of the 'celestial sphere'. Regardless of distance, we create a sphere around us onto which everything spacey is projected. You could even include planes or birds if you so wished.

CELESTIAL LATITUDE

The celestial sphere works much like mapping on Earth. As you'll remember from geography lessons at school, to locate something down here we use latitude and longitude. The equator is the most famous line of latitude and is the starting point for

measuring northward or southward – we call this 0° latitude. We use degrees (°) because when we locate places on Earth, or on the celestial sphere, it's done using angular measurements. Latitude increases as we move round the Earth northwards or southwards, reaching a maximum of 90°N at the North Pole and 90°S at the South Pole.

Lines of longitude, meanwhile, start from the North Pole and run 'down' Earth, crossing the equator and ending at the South Pole. These locate things east to west on the plane and are also measured in degrees. Here, of course, longitude crosses all the points around the equator (a circle), amounting to 360° in total. Actually, we move westward up to 180° and eastward 180°, but it all adds up to 360° in the end.

For the celestial sphere, we throw the whole latitude and longitude Earth grid up into the sky – it's a mirror image. There's no reason why we couldn't have used celestial latitude and celestial longitude as titles, but those who know better decided otherwise. So instead – and I cannot apologise enough – we have 'declination' for latitude and 'right ascension' for longitude.

Not only can the location of any object be described by its right ascension (RA) and declination (Dec.), but when you get down to looking at the paths of objects across the celestial sphere, you can understand some interesting things about how Earth moves, works and relates to the rest of space.

MEASURING THE SKY

Hands and fingers are very useful for getting to grips with sizes in the sky. Assume the following are held out at arm's length: an outstretched hand spans around 22°, which is close to the length of the Plough. Your fist is around 10°, while your thumb covers 2°. We seem to get the impression the full Moon is a lot bigger in the sky than it really is, but amazingly, the end of your little finger (again, at arm's length) is around 1°, which means it will cover the full Moon twice!

THE CELESTIAL
SPHERE

This has a grid which is the starry version of latitude and longitude on Earth

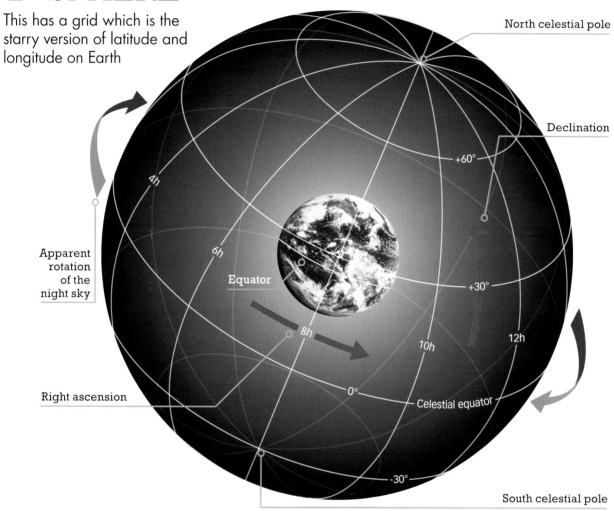

North celestial pole

Declination

+60°

Apparent
rotation
of the
night sky

6h

4h

Equator

+30°

Right ascension

8h

10h

12h

0°

Celestial equator

-30°

South celestial pole

For example, crossing the celestial equator at two points is the 'ecliptic'. This line represents the path of the Sun through the year, with the tilt due to Earth's changing tilt in relation to the Sun. When the Sun (ecliptic line) crosses the celestial equator northwards it not only represents the first day of spring (known as the vernal equinox in the northern hemisphere), but it also defines the zero point for the entire grid – we call this 0 hours right ascension and 0° declination. See the 'Using charts' box, left, for a full explanation of how this works – and then happy hunting!

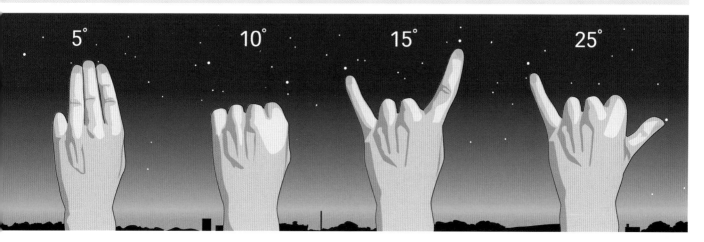

5°   10°   15°   25°

STAR CHARTS

ONCE YOU'VE MASTERED THE IDEA OF STAR CO-ORDINATES, THESE MAPS OF THE NIGHT SKY ARE INVALUABLE

Maps are among my favourite things. They let me know what can be found where and whether it is of interest to me. Of course, there are maps of differing scales, providing more or less detail, and I'll choose the map I need for the task at hand.

I may just want to know what part of America Minneapolis is in... or I may need to check which oak tree to turn right at, in order to find the hedge to follow to get to some megalithic standing stones. Once at the stones, if I look closely, they may reveal some astronomical event or depiction of the heavens carved or painted by some ancient people! Cave paintings dating back over 10,000 years in the south of France and some of the petroglyphs (rock art) in the deserts of America could be considered our earliest forms of star maps.

How far we've come since then. Today's star maps, found in astronomical books, are plotted by computer from data collected by spacecraft. We'll look at these in more detail shortly.

CHART-BUSTING

Don't dismiss old charts and maps as they contain a wealth of fascinating historical information. They feature forgotten constellations or those that have changed their names, as well as grand artwork and indications of the society's culture at the time.

One thing that has not changed in our modern scientifically accurate charts is how the brighter stars are shown by the biggest dots. All stars are, of course, the same-sized single points of light in the real night sky, but it is impossible to show their brightness any other way on a printed page. Our brains do seem to cope with this 'fudge' quite nicely. In fact, it's something you may never have thought about.

The other thing to consider is the projection: when a three-dimensional sky dome is flattened and warped down onto a piece of paper. Take a look at one of the finest star charty-things around – a planisphere – and you'll see what I mean. In an effort to squash the sky flat, the constellations are stretched out around the edge and look very different from the real sky. This is also a problem with all-sky monthly charts found in astronomy magazines. Again, this is something most of us can cope with, but for beginners it can initially seem quite odd when the real constellations look different from the printed ones. Nonetheless, a planisphere is a bit of kit that you'll always find useful.

But there's more to atlases than just star positions and brightness – although they are, of course, vitally important if you're trying to learn the sky. With symbols that don't detract from the

α	β	γ	δ	ε	ζ	η	θ	ι	κ	λ	μ
Alpha	Beta	Gamma	Delta	Epsilon	Zeta	Eta	Theta	Iota	Kappa	Lamda	Mu

IT'S ALL **GREEK TO US**

Who was the first person to map the sky? Why do constellations have a Latin possessive? Time to learn your Alpha, Beta, Gamma

The idea of understanding the sky was in evidence during Greek times. Most of the information we have about their thinking and constellation designs comes from a giant multi-volume work, *The Almagest* (also known as *The Great Syntaxis Of Astronomy*), by the mathematician and astronomer Ptolemy around 150 AD. Well over a thousand years later this 'book' found its way to Italy and was translated into Latin, which is why we have Latin names for the constellations.

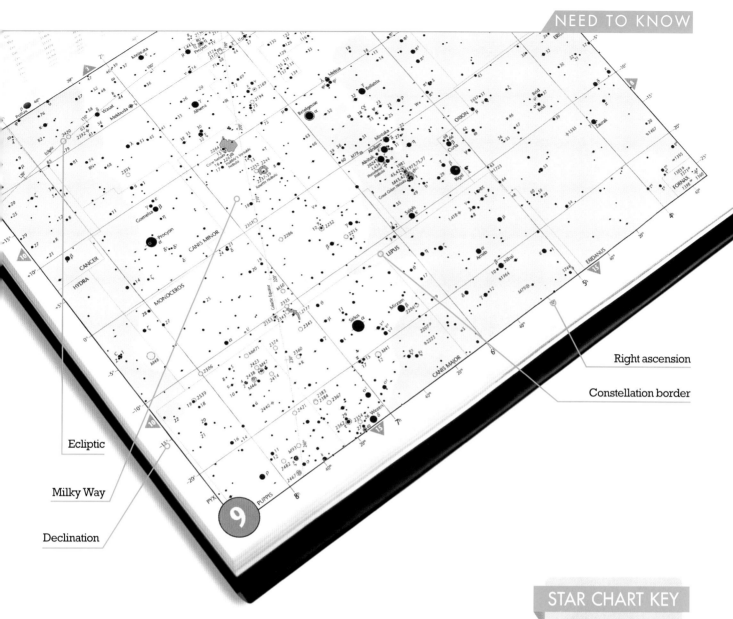

Right ascension

Constellation border

Ecliptic

Milky Way

Declination

overall view, you can identify stars that are variable (change in brightness) or double (optically or gravitationally together in the sky).

Depending on your atlas there may also be additional symbols for deep-sky objects such as nebulae, galactic star clusters, globular clusters, planetary nebulae and galaxies.

But let's go back to map scales. A useful atlas should have charts that vary in detail. You may, for example, have general seasonal charts or monthly charts, close-ups of some constellations and possibly a location chart for some of the deep-sky objects. As a beginner it's probably the seasonal or monthly charts that you'll use the most, so make sure you're happy with the style.

If you're technologically up to speed, a great way of creating star charts is by using computer software. A large number of programs are available (some of them free) that allow you to zoom in and out and have the added benefit of positioning the planets and the Moon for any day you wish. Computers do have their limitations, though: they can run out of power, they don't like dew and they crash. You don't get that with a magazine!

ν	ξ	ο	π	ρ	σ	τ	υ	φ	χ	ψ	ω
Nu	Xi	Omicron	Pi	Rho	Sigma	Tau	Upsilon	Phi	Chi	Psi	Omega

Other astronomers have also had their turn at ordering the stars, which up until the early 17th century were mainly known by Arabic names. Johann Bayer, in homage to the earlier Greek astronomers, labelled the brightest stars of a constellation with Greek letters – usually, but not always, assigning alpha to the brightest, then beta, gamma, all the way to omega. Using Ursa Major as an example, the Arabic star Dubhe is not the brightest in the constellation but was labelled by Bayer as alpha, and so is formally called Alpha Ursae Majoris. You'll notice that the last two words are spelt differently – they are the Latin for 'belonging to Ursa Major'. All constellations have a Latin possessive, such as Geminorum for 'belonging to Gemini'.

Each of the constellations also has its own three-letter abbreviation: Ursa Major's is UMa so Dubhe, again, would be α UMa.

EARTH'S AXIS
It tilts from the
vertical by 23.5°

NORTHERN
SPRING EQUINOX
Day and night are the same length

THE SUN

APHELION
Earth 152.1 million km
from the Sun

NORTHERN
SUMMER SOLSTICE
The longest day

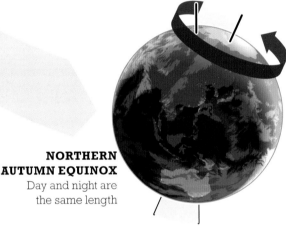

NORTHERN
AUTUMN EQUINOX
Day and night are
the same length

OUR PLACE
IN SPACE

HOW EARTH'S ANNUAL TRIP AROUND THE SUN GIVES RISE TO THE FOUR SEASONS

EARTH ORB T ILLUSTRATION BY ADRIAN DEAN, CHARTS BY PETE LAWRENCE

We take it for granted that Earth is spinning and travels around the Sun. We have to, because there is no way any of us can feel the spin or the speed of movement of our planet as it travels through space.

Cast your mind back to when you were seven years old. You've been told that the reason the Sun crosses the sky is because Earth is turning on its axis once a day. And before you've had time to take this in you're informed that Earth takes a year to travel round the Sun. Then, after primary school, you're introduced to some numbers. For instance, the average speed of Earth through space (following its orbit) is just under 30km/s, which is nearly 108,000km/h (67,000mph). And the rotation of our planet, though slower, still

makes you think. Standing on the equator, you'll be travelling at over 1,600km/h (1,000mph).

FOUR SEASONS

Earth's path around the Sun isn't all about maximum speeds, though. Let's take a look at the seasons. Many think we get spring, summer, autumn and winter because of the distance Earth is from the Sun. Indeed, the Earth does have a slightly elliptical orbit, which leads to a distance difference of 5 million km between Earth's closest point to the Sun (perihelion), and its furthest point (aphelion) – but this doesn't give rise to the seasons. You might be surprised to know that during

JOURNEY ROUND
THE SUN

On its way round the Sun, the Earth spins on a tilted axis. Either the northern or southern hemisphere gets more direct sunlight, causing the seasons

PERIHELION
Earth 147.1 million km from the Sun

NORTHERN WINTER SOLSTICE
The shortest day

DAY AND NIGHT
Earth spins on its axis once every 23.93 hours

A YEAR
Earth orbits the Sun in 365.26 days

THE CHANGING NIGHT SKY

To understand why the constellations shift around the sky, we first need to consider the length of a day. Not the regular day of 24 hours, however, which is called the solar day and is the time it takes the Earth to spin once on its axis in relation to the Sun. No, there's another day, called the sidereal day.

This is based on the Earth's rotation with respect to the stars, and it's 3 minutes 56 seconds shorter than the solar day. This difference is due to the fact that the Earth, as well as spinning on its axis, also orbits the Sun. This time difference between the solar and sidereal days, although short, causes the stars to rise almost four minutes earlier each day and is why the constellations change in the sky through the year.

15 DECEMBER, 7PM — ORION — E S W

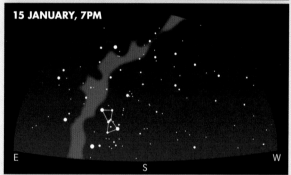

15 JANUARY, 7PM — E S W

15 MARCH, 7PM — E S W

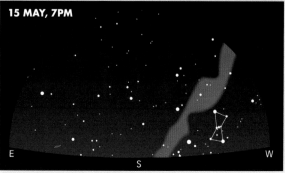

15 MAY, 7PM — E S W

the northern hemisphere's winter, Earth is as close to the Sun as it can get: perihelion happens around 3 January.

The seasons are in fact due to Earth spinning on a tilted axis as it moves around the Sun, which varies the intensity of sunlight hitting each hemisphere throughout the year. Model globes of Earth show this: they lean by 23.5° from the vertical. You can see this lean in relation to our orbital path around the Sun in the diagram above.

At times, the North Pole tilts 23.5° towards the Sun, while the South Pole points away by the same amount. For the northern hemisphere, the day this happens is the longest day (the summer solstice) around 20 June and for the southern hemisphere it's the shortest day (the winter solstice). Six months later, the tilt is reversed so that the South Pole points towards the Sun and the North Pole leans away into space. This marks the shortest day in the northern hemisphere and the longest day in the southern hemisphere (around 21 December).

As it goes round the Sun, Earth's axis always tilts in the same direction in relation to the stars. In the northern hemisphere you can see this by the fact that the star Polaris is always in the same place overhead due north.

The spin of Earth and its motion around the Sun doesn't just create the seasons. It also explains why our view of the constellations changes over the year.

SEEING AND ATMOSPHERIC TRANSPARENCY

HOW THE ATMOSPHERE CAN AFFECT YOUR ABILITY TO OBSERVE STARS AND PLANETS TO A SURPRISING EXTENT

The weather is generally considered to be the biggest hindrance to astronomy. What's the betting that the night you decide to use your new telescope is the night that spell of fine weather changes for the worse? So you'd have thought that when the skies finally clear, your problems would be over. Surprisingly, though, even a clear night may not be the best time to go out and observe.

The issue is the 'seeing'. In astronomy, this doesn't mean how you look at something. It's a term that describes how much the view you see through your telescope is disturbed by what's going on in the atmosphere above you.

At times of good seeing, you'll get sharp, steady views through your telescope. But bad seeing produces turbulent, unstable telescope views of the Moon and shuddering, shaky images of stars. This is thanks to the layers of moving air between you and the object you're looking at, the effects of which are magnified by your telescope. On the other hand, deep-sky objects like galaxies and nebulae aren't as badly affected by bad seeing.

In the atmosphere, air at different temperatures is always moving around and mixing together. Light travels through hot and cold air at different speeds, so it is continually bent this way and that before it finally arrives at your scope all shaken and stirred. Sometimes there are very few moments of clarity. One of the best ways to see this distortion is to watch the Sun setting on a clear horizon. It will have a jagged appearance, thanks to the sunlight moving through layers of turbulent air.

The setting Sun appears to have a jagged edge because you see its light through a turbulent atmosphere

IMPROVE YOUR SEEING

You can't do anything about 'high-level seeing' – the air currents far above you – but you can influence the 'low-level seeing' to create steadier air conditions immediately around you and your scope. Here's how:

›1 Leave your scope outside to cool to the ambient temperature, eliminating any air currents in the tube.

›2 Observe on grass rather than concrete. Concrete absorbs more heat from the Sun and radiates it out to the air above it for longer.

›3 Air currents tend to stay low to the ground, so it can be a good idea to raise up your scope on a platform.

›4 If you build an observatory, make it using thin materials like wood that can cool quickly.

›5 The geography of your observing site affects how air behaves. Being near the sea gives you calmer air than if you're near a range of hills, where air is forced upwards, causing turbulence.

Placing your setup on grass can reduce air turbulence around your scope

THE ANTONIADI SCALE

It's very useful to note down what the seeing is when you're observing. Many astronomers use the Antoniadi Scale as a measure of what the atmosphere is up to. It's a five-point scale using Roman numerals. I indicates the best conditions, while V describes the worst.

I Perfect seeing, without any quiver of turbulence whatsoever.

II Slight shimmers; moments of stillness last several seconds.

III Average seeing; larger air tremors blur the view.

IV Poor views, with constant troublesome undulations of the image.

V Bad views with severe undulations; so unstable that even quick sketches are out of the question.

The other factor that affects observing conditions is the transparency of the night – just how clear the sky is. After it's been raining, the sky is completely transparent because the rain clears away particles of dust and smog from the air. However, when it's been raining it also tends to be windy, which means that the seeing is bad. You'll notice that the stars are twinkling because of this. Transparent conditions are however good for large, faint objects like nebulae and galaxies, which really benefit from the better contrast. Poor transparency generally means the air is steady with good seeing, but dust and particles are sitting in the atmosphere because the air is still. These conditions are good for looking at the Moon and stars.

A good way to think of it is to imagine a swimming pool with a penny coin on the bottom. The water represents our atmosphere and the coin the starry object you're looking at. Through completely still water with no currents, the coin looks still, crisp and clear. In this case the seeing is perfect and so is the transparency. If the water is made to move – causing ripples – the coin's image will shake around; the transparency is still good but the seeing is bad. And if some milk is spilt in the pool so you can't see the coin very clearly, the transparency will be reduced.

It goes to show that you're at the mercy of the atmosphere... and that moments of clarity are a wonderful thing.

14 FEBRUARY, 9PM

NGC 188 4.2 Polaris 7.1 6.5 2.0 6.7 6.3 5.6 6.4 5.9 5.2 4.7 4.4

URSA MINOR 4.8 4.2 6.4 4.3

4.3 5.2 Kochab 2.1

5.6

5.0 5.5 6.1 Pherkad 3.1

5.0 = magnitude

N

HOW FAINT CAN YOU SEE?

Atmospheric conditions have an impact on the faintness of the stars you can observe. Use the chart here to check the faintest stars you can see by looking at Ursa Minor on a very clear night to work out your limiting magnitude. This is the faintest star magnitude, or brightness, that you can see from your location – higher numbers mean fainter stars.

Work out your limiting magnitude by finding the dimmest stars you can see in Ursa Minor, as described below. Under a perfect sky you should be able to spot mag +6.5 stars

LIGHT POLLUTION

THE INTRUSIVE EFFECTS OF LIGHT POLLUTION ARE EVERY ASTRONOMER'S BUGBEAR. WE LOOK AT THE CAUSES AND EFFECTS OF THIS IRRITANT

One of the biggest problems facing astronomers today is light pollution. It's caused by the vast array of street lighting and light from buildings, which scatters light off particles in the atmosphere. In the worst cases, this causes the night to take on an unearthly orange glow. From some places the effect of light pollution can be to virtually wash away any evidence that there is a wondrous vista lurking behind it. Add in a dollop of hazy weather and your viewing gets even worse, as the light gets bounced around even more.

Not surprisingly, the worst places for light pollution are the major towns and cities. However, stargazers who live in more rural locations can be just as bothered by the annoying bright light from a neighbour's badly-adjusted single security light. One light can be just as terrible as an entire city when it comes to observing. Wherever you are, the problem is getting worse as towns spread and people feel they need more protection for their homes.

With increasing light pollution, the grandeur of the night sky has gradually been eroded. As light pollution increases, the number of stars you can see decreases. This is all described by limiting magnitude – ie, what is the faintest star visible? In very dark locations the eye can see stars just below mag +6.0 (the higher the number, the fainter the star), but with more lights around, this can be reduced to a handful of only the brightest first magnitude stars.

The biggest casualty is the band of the Milky Way, the band of stars that stretches high across the autumn skies. It has a brightness of around mag +4.5. This makes it accessible from darker suburban locations, but washed away if you're in a place with more lighting around. As more people now live in towns and cities, an increasing number of people have never seen the Milky Way.

COUNTRY WISE

Other objects that suffer include those that appear as fuzzy patches in the sky, namely nebulae, star clusters and galaxies. So if you live in the countryside, you're probably able to see such deep-sky wonders as the Orion Nebula, the Sword Handle double cluster in Perseus and the Andromeda Galaxy – but if you live in a city, you are limited to viewing the brightest stars and the planets.

Needless to say, if you are hampered by light pollution, then you can always place your telescope carefully in the car and drive off to a dark site. Maybe you'd like to try one of the five dark sky sites that we've identified in the UK on the map to the left? One of them is the Galloway Forest Park, which in 2009 was designated as the UK's first Dark Sky Park.

And if you're confined to your garden? Never fear – just take a look at our four tips that should help lessen the effects of light pollution.

HOW TO BEAT LIGHT POLLUTION

Don't be a victim of the glare! Here are four ways to reduce the effects of sky glow

Position your telescope so that it's shielded from the effects of a direct light source.
It's surprising how well you can overcome local light pollution by simply repositioning your scope in the garden. Find a position that is hidden from the view of nearby street or security lights by moving closer to a fence or wall.

Make sure your eyes are properly dark adapted before viewing.
Improve your chances of seeing fainter magnitudes by making sure your eyes are fully dark-adapted before you go outside. Get a red light torch ready and turn off house lights for at least 15 minutes. Keep them off so they don't light up your garden.

Reduce the glare by asking your neighbours to temporarily turn off their security lights.
Are you friendly with your neighbours? If it's their security light that streams into your garden, invite them round to look through your scope and they might get the message when they see a lighthouse shining in their face!

Buy light pollution filters.
Light pollution filters come in an array of types, depending on what light you want to block out (eg sodium and mercury) and exactly what you want to enhance. They are also known as nebula filters, as these are the objects they work for. You can buy one for around £20.

5 **DARK** SKY SITES

>**1** Galloway Forest Park, **Scotland**
www.forestry.gov.uk/darkskygalloway

>**2** Kelling Heath, **Norfolk**
www.kellingheath.co.uk

>**3** Kielder Forest, **Northumberland**
www.visitkielder.com

>**4** Dartmoor National Park, **Devon**
www.dartmoor-npa.gov.uk

>**5** Brecon Beacons National Park, **Wales**
www.breconbeacons.org

Red and yellow areas are high in light pollution. Grey areas boast no adverse effects and are prime locations for observing

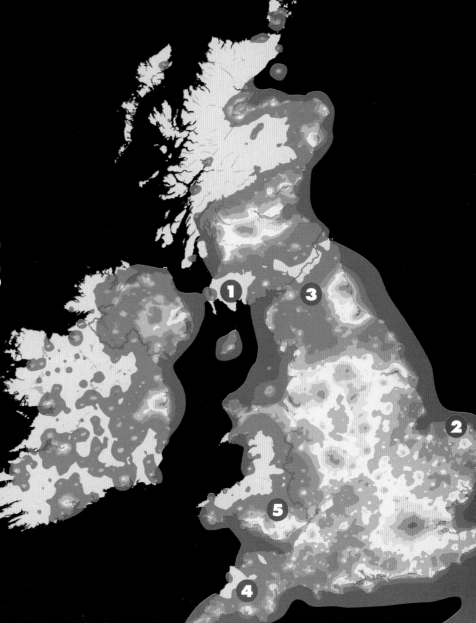

KEEPING AN OBSERVING LOG

HOW TO REALLY 'OBSERVE' THE NIGHT SKY AND GET MORE FROM ASTRONOMY BY RECORDING WHAT YOU SEE

Today's modern telescopes make it easy for you to whizz through your Go-To list of deep-sky wonders in no time at all. You might think that the idea of actually stopping on an object for 15 minutes or so, especially to draw the thing or at least be able to describe it in detail, seems a little old-fashioned. If this is the way you practise astronomy, then you can certainly say that you've seen any given object – but you haven't truly 'observed' it.

To fully appreciate the sky, there is nothing like an observing log – a journal in which you detail information, observations and thoughts during an observing session. There are many reasons to keep a log, as you'll see from the case studies below, including Patrick Moore who has over five decades of logs. But overall, by paying attention to and recording what you are looking at, your observing improves. You get better at seeing finer details and viewing seemingly invisible features. By taking time, objects take on a new light, which adds a great deal to your experience.

You may have seen wonderful observing logs from a dedicated few, and it might seem daunting to try and follow their example. But your logbook doesn't need to be an ornate affair – just begin with some basic details. At the very least you should record the date, time and object you're looking at, what telescope and magnification you're using and some notes about the object. When you're happy that you've got the hang of covering the basics, you can add details like light pollution, sky transparency, limiting magnitude and any telescope filters used.

Drawings are a bonus and can really enhance your logbook entry. Once you become a seasoned observer, you may not even need to do the full sketch at the telescope – just do a rough drawing and complete it indoors as soon as possible after the session is over. Indeed, many astronomers use a pocket notebook to jot down some records outside before transcribing observations into a nice hardback, A4-sized logbook.

The book keepers

Observers keep logbooks for lots of different reasons. Here, one very famous astronomer and a keen amateur share some insights into what they keep them for and the best way to log your observations

PATRICK MOORE
SELSEY, WEST SUSSEX
Patrick offers his tips on keeping a logbook
In astronomical work it is essential to be systematic. Your log should show what you have observed and what you need to observe next.

This can also be a help to other observers studying the same or similar objects. In the late 1950s, radio waves from Jupiter were detected.

Analysts wanted to find out whether they came from the core or from discrete surface features, and they needed central meridian transit times for features such as the Great Red Spot and smaller white spots from 1946 to 1963. I was able to provide these details from my Jupiter logbook (pictured above).

A logbook entry should include the objects you observed, the equipment used, the time in GMT, the quality of the seeing and any special circumstances. It is very useful to include illustrations. I used to make a sketch at the telescope, 'tidy it up' and then re-check it at the telescope. You should also keep a separate book or file for each object: the Moon, Jupiter, variable stars and so on. And never send away an original observation – always send a copy.

MARTIN McKENNA
MAGHERA, N. IRELAND
Martin has been keeping an observing log for 11 years
The logbook is more than a collection of text and sketches: it documents the growth and change of the person who penned it through the passage of time, and it's only through reading such a record that you can appreciate just where someone is within their observing career, and where they need to go next.

For me personally, keeping an observing log is about capturing memories of spectacular sky events and recording those events in your own style so that they can be relived with a smile at some point in the future. I record everything in the sky that is of interest to me. This includes transient astronomical, weather and atmospheric events during day and night.

I also like to complement observations with details that may seem trivial to some but that I know will raise a smile when I re-read them myself. The antics of my cat often feature – like the time when it jumped on the telescope one night, causing it to swing frantically to the zenith.

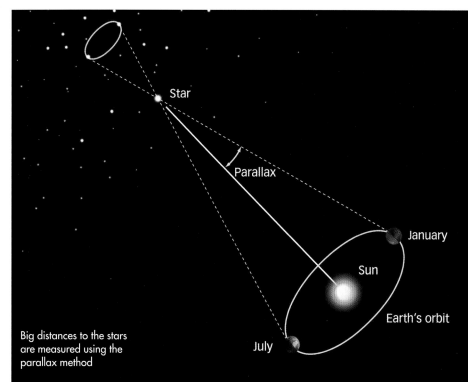

Star

Parallax

January

Sun

Earth's orbit

July

Big distances to the stars are measured using the parallax method

HOW FAR
ARE STARS?

For measuring the big distances to the stars, astronomers use something called parallax. This involves watching a close star's movement against the fixed background of much more distant stars. It's like holding up your index finger at arms' length and viewing it against the background through your left eye and then your right – there is a position shift between each view because your finger is much closer than the background.

This is how it works in space, too, except our two views are six months apart, when Earth is on either side of its orbit around the Sun. This is the widest possible separation we can get between our telescopic 'eyes', and even then the shifts are so small that this technique only works accurately out to a few hundred lightyears.

DISTANCES IN SPACE

HOW CAN WE EVEN ATTEMPT TO DESCRIBE THE MIND-BOGGLING DISTANCES BETWEEN STARS?

REFLECTING RADIO WAVES

The Lovell Radio Telescope at Jodrell Bank in Cheshire was used to measure the distance of Venus by bouncing radio waves off the planet. Just like the technique for the Moon (see p30), it involves measuring the time it takes for a burst of radio waves to come back. Of course, Venus is farther away than the Moon: the lunar laser is back in three seconds, while the journey to Venus and back is four minutes.

Stepping into the garden on one of those crisp clear nights, I see sparkling stars and a crescent Moon about to set near the western horizon. Saturn's up there, Jupiter's over here and there goes a shooting star. Fantastic.

What is just as amazing is the fact that I cannot tell which of these objects is the closest or furthest away from me. Knowing that the star Aldebaran is over nine million times more distant than the Moon does not really compute anyway – these distances are too big for my brain.

As far as locating objects in the sky is concerned, we project them onto an invisible great glass thing around us called the celestial sphere. It's useful and it works, and most of the time we're really not bothered how far away something is anyway. But what if we are?

The first thing to realise – and I mentioned the problem with thinking about the sizes – is that

big distances need a big scale: several of them in fact. We would use centimetres or inches to measure the length of a bookcase (for astronomy books, of course), but that would not make any sense when trying to explain the distance from Glasgow to Belfast. So kilometres or miles are our Earthly scale of things.

INCREASINGLY UNWIELDY

Journeying into space, with the close Moon at around 384,000km (250,000 miles) or the nearby Sun at 150 million km (93 million miles), you can see that these units become more and more unwieldy the further we go. Saying, "Oh, that's 83 thousand million squillion zillion km away" is not that useful and takes up a lot of time, when you could just say, "Oh, that's three zarquons." Admittedly, I made that last unit up, but I'm sure that you get the point.

So, kilometres or miles are confined to the Solar System. We could use something better, but we're safe and happy with them and there's some continuity with how we do things on Earth without getting too space-ified too early on.

The other 'something better' is simply a unit based on Earth's mean distance from the Sun – instead of it being 150 million km we can say it is one astronomical unit or 1 AU. Using this method, all the planets, and anything else flying around the Sun (or Earth) can be defined in terms of an astronomical unit. For example, Jupiter is about 5 AU from the Sun; that's five times farther from the Sun than Earth. Travelling out farther, the nearest star, Proxima Centauri, is around 268,000 AU away. You'll have gathered that the numbers are growing again, which means we need to switch to another scale – the one that is used by all but the hardiest of scientists. Enter, stage right, the lightyear.

This wonderful length is simply the distance that light travels in one year. Speeding along at almost 300,000 kilometres per second (186,282 miles per second), light can cover 9,460,000,000,000 (9.46 trillion) km, or 5,860,000,000,000 (5.86 trillion) miles in a year. With this unit at hand we can say that Proxima Centauri is 4.26 lightyears away.

TRAVELS WITH LIGHT

Looking into the night sky, most of the stars we see are tens to hundreds of lightyears away, although there are a few that reach into the thousands. When we think about how light travels from a star that is, say, 80 lightyears away, we realise that we are seeing that star as it appeared 80 years ago.

The light has been travelling through space for all that time before it ends up in our eyes; therefore, when we gaze into space what we are actually doing is looking back in time.

Don't think this means any of the stars are not there any longer. Stars live for millions, if not billions, of years, so even a star that is 5,000 lightyears away in the night sky is still really shining away quite happily.

MIRRORS ON THE MOON

The Apollo astronauts left laser retroreflectors on the lunar surface

Nowadays the distance to the Moon is easy to measure, thanks to the Apollo astronauts, who left some experiments there back in the early 1970s. These were the marvellously named 'lunar laser ranging retroreflector arrays' – mirrors, to you and me. These mirrors have been used constantly ever since, and are now the longest working Apollo lunar experiments.

A laser beam from Earth is fired at one of the mirrors, which reflects it. The time it takes to get there and back gives you the distance to the Moon, if you know the speed of light. From these measurements we know the distance to the Moon: 405,696km (252,088 miles) when it's furthest away, and 363,104km (225,622 miles) when it's closest. We also know that the Moon is moving away from us at about 4cm (1.5 inches) per year.

THE SOLAR SYSTEM
AND BEYOND

Local distances are measured by the time it takes light to get there

MOON
1.5 lightseconds

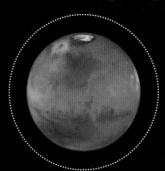

MARS
5.4 lightminutes

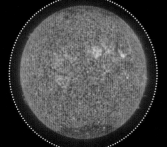

SUN
8.3 lightminutes

PLUTO
5.5 lighthours

PROXIMA CENTAURI
4.26 lightyears

Some of the more distant red galaxies in this Hubble picture are nearly 13 billion lightyears from Earth

VARIABLE STARS

Most of the stars we see shine away quite happily – their brightness in the night remains reassuringly constant. These, thankfully, include the Sun. However there are some that, for various reasons, appear to get brighter and fainter over time. These are the variable stars.

First catalogued in the early 17th century, variables have played an important part in measuring the Universe. The most useful are called Cepheid variables. What makes them so splendid is that the time they take to change from bright to dim and back (their period) is very regular, and related to how truly bright they are. If you know how bright a star is (its absolute magnitude), then by simply measuring its brightness in the sky (apparent magnitude) you can calculate its distance. So in this way, we can work out how far distant galaxies are just by looking for variable stars in them. Easy!

The M100 galaxy's Cepheid variables tell us that it's 56 million lightyears away

MEASURING SPACE

THERE'S MORE TO HOW ASTRONOMERS CALCULATE THE SPACE BETWEEN OBJECTS IN THE NIGHT SKY

So now you know all about distances in space, and how our Earthly metres and feet are not much use, as they turn into impractically large numbers with lots of zeroes, like 56,000,000,000,000,000,000,000km – that's 56 quintillion km. Now, a 'quintillion' doesn't mean anything to me; add on a few squillions and it's all uncharted territory. You know that to make life easier when measuring distances across the Solar System, we use the astronomical unit (AU), which is the mean Earth to Sun distance. And, for the next stage (all the way to the 'edge' of the Universe, in fact) we use the lightyear. One lightyear is, of course, simply the distance that light travels in one year.

That's all well and good, but the missing ingredient is how do you measure space and how much space have we actually found out there? This brings us to the things that fundamentally altered our understanding of space – the telescope, subsequent associated measuring devices and the use of non-visual wavelengths like infrared and ultraviolet. Without these we would still be oblivious to the nature of the Universe.

EXPLOSION OF KNOWLEDGE

The first explosion of knowledge came with precision telescopes that enabled us to view the minute shifts of nearby stars against the more distant 'fixed' stars, which in reality is caused by Earth's movement around the Sun. It's like looking at your finger with one eye and then the other, noticing how your finger's position has changed relative to the background. Parallax, as the system is known, was first successfully used in 1838 when Friedrich Bessel calculated the distance to the naked-eye star 61 Cygni (in Cygnus, the Swan) to be just over 11 lightyears.

Today, of course, astronomers and scientists don't need to look through a telescope in the cold night; they employ spacecraft in order to do all of the measuring stuff for them. Up above the wobbling, swirling impreciseness that Earth's atmosphere gives us, spacecraft can 'see' much better and with much more precision. For example, from 1989 until 1993 the European Space Agency's Hipparchos mission measured the parallax of over 118,000 stars out to nearly 500 lightyears from Earth. Try that with a telescope down here and you'll be lucky to get out to 100 lightyears, and even then you'd doubt the accuracy of the outer stars. Plus, there's no way you can get through as many stars as a robotic spacecraft – not without endless cups of tea, or getting incredibly bored.

Five hundred lightyears, eh? That's not a very big bag of peanuts as far as space is concerned. In fact, it's like going for a short jog with your dog to the garden gate and back. Look at our Galaxy:

its centre is about 30,000 lightyears away in the direction of Sagittarius; the whole kit and caboodle is over 100,000 lightyears across. So 500 lightyears is still in our back garden.

NEAREST NEIGHBOURS

Our Galaxy is part of a Local Group of some 30 galaxies – some large, such as our own and M33, but many far smaller, such as the Wolf-Lundmark-Melotte Galaxy in Cetus, or the Magellanic Clouds. The closest galaxy is the Andromeda Galaxy, visible as a smudge to the unaided eye, sitting at a distance of around 2.8 million lightyears. That's still peanuts. The whole Local Group is around 10 million lightyears in size. Still peanuts, but only just. Farther out (and there's still a long way to go) our Group belongs to the Virgo Supercluster – a large rounded curtain shape that stretches over 200 million lightyears.

You may be wondering how we can measure these vast distances. Well, it's by using special kinds of variable stars, some of which do spectacular things (see 'Variable stars', p31). Plus, on large scales, we see that most galaxies are 'moving away' from us, and the further we look, the faster they seem to be travelling. This is all a part of the famous 'redshift' (see below), which has enabled us to calculate the size of our visible Universe as 13.7 billion lightyears across.

PAUL WOOTTON

REDSHIFT

How the 'stretching' of space helps us to measure it more accurately

Imagine a very big rubber band, as wide as a road and as long as you fancy. Onto this rubber band, at some distance apart, place two cars. Now with two helpers at each end of the band, start to pull. You can envisage what will start to happen: the fabric of the band will start to stretch. What's

happening to the cars? They are beginning to move apart, not because they themselves are moving, but because the rubber between them is stretching.

This is exactly what happens in space, on a much larger scale. We see galaxies appearing to move away from us, when in

reality it is the space in-between stretching. This has an effect on the light we get from the distant galaxy – it is being stretched too.

This is much like hearing a police car siren sound 'dropping' as it passes us by (the famous Doppler effect). That's caused by the sound wavelength being

stretched out as it zooms away. In the case of waves of light, this stretching turns the light more and more red (visible red wavelengths are the longest), hence the name redshift. And simply (with maths again!), the greater the degree of redshift, the further away the galaxy in question must be.

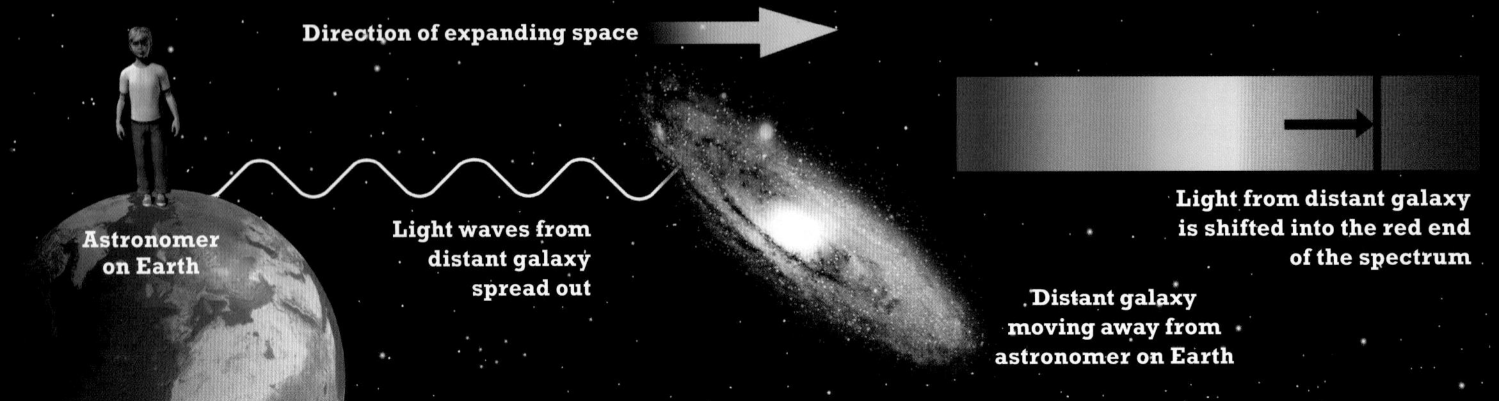

Direction of expanding space

Astronomer on Earth

Light waves from distant galaxy spread out

Distant galaxy moving away from astronomer on Earth

Light from distant galaxy is shifted into the red end of the spectrum

WHAT TO USE

SEE FARTHER INTO SPACE BY USING BINOCULARS AND TELESCOPES

When you start your stargazing quest, you need do nothing more than walk outside on a clear night and look up. But there'll come a time when you feel you need to get closer to the view – it happens to us all! And for this you'll need a pair of binoculars or a telescope.

These pieces of optical equipment do two things: firstly they collect more light from the dim and distant stars than your eyes alone do, and secondly they magnify the view.

In this section, we'll take you through the best types of equipment to train on the night skies. We'll look at why it's best to begin with binoculars before moving on to a telescope, and why the mount that a telescope tube sits on is every bit as important as the lenses or mirrors that gather up all that starlight.

We'll also take a tour of the important accessories you need to get great views, such as eyepieces, finderscopes and filters, as well as showing how to use all this equpiment and what kind of views you can expect of the skies above.

BUYERS' GUIDE

There are two kinds of binoculars: the classic Porro-prism style used by astronomers, and the more compact roof-prism style, used mainly for watching wildlife.

If you're looking to buy binoculars, first check you can get a really sharp focus with them, using something that is really far away. If you wear glasses, check that you can still focus the binoculars without them.

You should measure the exit pupils of your binoculars. These are the illuminated circles you'll see in each of the eyepieces when you hold the binoculars away from your eyes. They should be 7mm or less in diameter, and the exit pupils should also be complete circles.

Next, look through the objective lenses and eyepieces for purple or orangey reflections inside the binoculars. These indicate that the surfaces of the prisms and lenses have been anti-reflection coated, which is desirable as you won't lose as much light as it travels through the instrument.

Prices for a 7x50 pair range from £20 to over £200. We'd sugest spending at least £50 or so, to ensure you're not stuck with anything you'll later regret buying.

DOUBLE VISION

BINOCULARS ARE AN ESSENTIAL PART OF AN ASTRONOMER'S TOOL KIT

Binoculars are a great tool for any observer, and to begin with there are only a few points worth considering. Having said that, do not let facts and figures and overly complicated suggestions get in the way when the stars are sparkling in a deep dark sky – get out there while the seeing is good!

I bet some of you have binoculars tucked away in a cupboard, used in some past age to watch that friendly robin perching photogenically on a nearby post box – but what about using them for space?

I've spoken to many people who have never thought about training their binoculars on the stars. If you don't have a pair, then ask a friend, a relation, a next-door neighbour – some will turn up somewhere. The fact that you may not need to pay anything at all in order to help your astronomical pursuit is what makes binoculars so good.

The overriding factor is doing something, so unless the binoculars are truly useless, like the cheap plastic ones that come in a children's spy kit, give them a go. I thoroughly recommend binoculars for any night-time starry skies adventure, whether you're a beginner or are pretty advanced.

BEFORE YOU BEGIN

If you're out learning the constellations for the very first time, then a glance through correctly adjusted binoculars will only tempt you to continue the journey. Some people may suggest that you should wait until you know your way around the sky without any optical aids before moving on to equipment. Frankly, this is barking mad: the more you are able to get in the stargazing mix, the better.

What binoculars do, of course, is make things bigger. With their big lenses, they magnify what you're looking at by grabbing more light than your

eye ever could. But before you dash outside, there are some points to consider.

Binoculars can be heavy, so holding them up may give both your head and arms some fine aches. Add in the magnification factor, and you'll find that it's not an easy task trying to hold them still enough for the image not to wobble all over the place.

Simple things will help in overcoming all of this: rest your arms on a fence or wall

if there is one nearby, or observe from a deckchair to support your neck. Some binoculars can also be fitted to a tripod (with an adaptor), which is another solution to the wobbly field of view.

Now that you're prepared for action, you can venture out with confidence. But with the whole firmament above you, what should you look at first? Here are a few ideas...

FIGURE IT OUT

Binoculars are normally specified by two numbers, such 10x50 ('10 by 50'). The first number, the '10', is the magnification you get, while the second

number, the '50', is the size in millimetres of the objective lenses. These are the ones at the big end of the binoculars, away from your eye.

A magnification of seven is really the smallest that is any use, and you can choose up to 10 before the wobble-factor becomes too great and you need to

start using a tripod. The bigger the objective lenses, the more light your eye gets and the fainter the objects you can see, but the binoculars will be heavier.

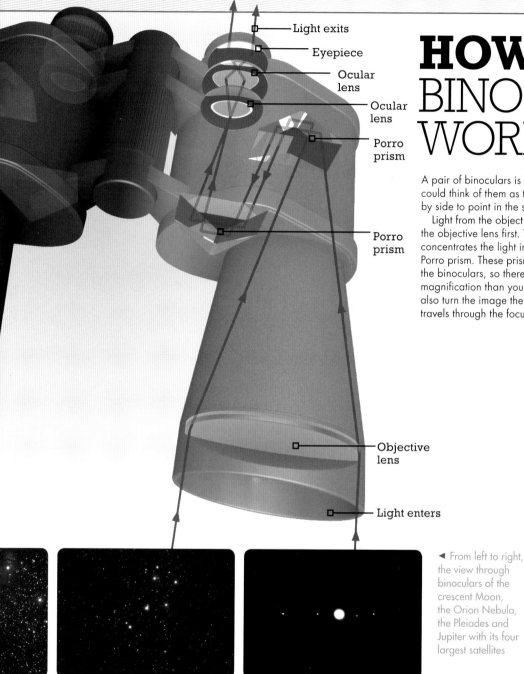

Light exits
Eyepiece
Ocular lens
Ocular lens
Porro prism
Porro prism
Objective lens
Light enters

HOW DO BINOCULARS WORK?

A pair of binoculars is basically a device to gather light. You could think of them as two identical telescopes strapped side by side to point in the same direction.

Light from the object you're looking at has to pass through the objective lens first. This is a convex piece of glass that concentrates the light into a beam that converges on the first Porro prism. These prisms optically fold the light path inside the binoculars, so there's a longer focal length and more magnification than you'd expect from the compact size. They also turn the image the right way round. After that, the light travels through the focusing lenses to end up at your eyes.

◀ From left to right, the view through binoculars of the crescent Moon, the Orion Nebula, the Pleiades and Jupiter with its four largest satellites

FINDING FOCUS

To get the best view through binoculars, adjust the eyepieces to fit the distance between your eyes and focus them both to give sharp views.

• ADJUSTING EYEPIECES To get the distance between the eyepieces to match the distance between your eyes, called the interpupillary distance, move the two halves of the binoculars around the central hinge until the view through both eyepieces is a clear circle.

• ADJUSTING FOCUS Close your right eye and look through the left eyepiece, then adjust the central focusing wheel to sharpen the view. Now close your left eye and look through the right eyepiece, which has its own focus adjustment. Turn this until you get a sharp focus. The view through both eyepieces will be sharp.

The Moon is a must. The eye shows light and dark areas, and several splats of impacts around craters, but binoculars reveal the craters themselves. Then there's the mountainous terrain, all brought into great relief by highlights and shadows created by the Sun's light. The best time to look at the Moon is between the crescent phase and the gibbous phase, when the Moon is more than half but less than fully lit up.

SEEING STAR BIRTH

If you look at the Orion Nebula with your eyes, all you'll see is a small smudge below the three belt stars of Orion (and if light pollution is bad where you live, sometimes not even that). But train your binoculars on it, and it will look like a delicate semi-circular curving structure with a bright centre. This is a stellar nursery made up of dust and gas, where more than 1,000 stars are currently being created.

Next, find the Pleiades in Taurus, one of the finest star clusters in the sky. To the eye, this looks like a close family of six or seven stars (though some people can see 12 or more), but with binoculars this number increases to around 40.

Finally, would you believe you can see another planet's moons? Jupiter's four main moons, Io, Europa, Ganymede and Callisto, will look like four little points of light through binoculars. Because the inner moons orbit in just a few days, it is possible to see some movement in the system over the course of a few hours. As for the planet itself, this just looks like a star when you see it with your eyes, but with binoculars you'll be able to see it as a disc of light – very exciting the first time you see it!

WHAT NEXT

Try out a few pairs of binoculars to compare them. Your local astronomy society is a good place to go. *Exploring The Night Sky With Binoculars* by Patrick Moore (Cambridge University Press, 2000) is also well worth reading.

SIMPLE TELESCOPES

ALL ABOUT REFLECTORS AND REFRACTORS

Here's a question for you: what is the only essential thing you need if you want to call yourself an astronomer? Is it a good knowledge of finding your way around the night sky? No. Is it a broad knowledge of the objects you can find in space, like black holes and nebulae? No. The answer is a telescope! Just a simple telescope.

It seems that is the perception of the subject, but of course that's not true. I have known many people who have decided astronomy is for them, and before doing anything that I'm about to describe below, out they go to buy a telescope that's entirely inappropriate. Predictably, it just sits around not doing much before it's sold on eBay.

THE RIGHT SCOPE FOR YOU

'Inappropriate' in this case means a scope that is the wrong size, shape or weight to make it useful to the owner. You may want a light, small scope that's easy to plonk on the garden table and impress party guests with fine views of the Moon. Or you may want something more sturdy that can track the stars as they move across the night sky, so you can photograph that distant galaxy 'Slight Fuzz 7HX-67F'. But the two are quite different beasts, and if you go out and make a purchase without

doing a little bit of homework first, it's unlikely you'll end up with the best scope for you.

So what do you do if you want a telescope? One of the best ideas is to visit, if not join, your local astronomical society. Many members will be very keen amateurs who'll not only show you a variety of scopes during one of their observing evenings, but if you do buy one, will be able to help you work out how the thing actually works.

Another place you can go to see a range of scopes is a recognised telescope dealer. Nearly all of these suppliers have staff who know what they're talking about and will be able to offer advice.

It's worth pointing out that the reverse is also true: if the shop selling telescopes also sells kettles and soft furnishings, then it's very likely the sales team are not themselves dedicated to astronomy, and they probably won't be able to answer any questions you might have.

Anyway, after all that, what exactly does a telescope do? Basically, it captures more light than your eye – just think about the much larger diameter of a telescope tube compared to the pupil of your eye. By 'playing' correctly with this large amount of light, the fainter objects of the Universe can be revealed to us, and objects that are too small

HOW DOES A
TELESCOPE WORK?

There are two basic designs: one uses lenses, the other uses mirrors

Eyepiece

Focus

Focal length

Starlight

Primary mirror

Lens

REFRACTOR
This type of telescope grabs all of its light with a lens at one end of a tube. The light is then focused down to the other end, where an eyepiece magnifies the image and throws it into your eye.

UPSIDE-DOWN IMAGE

CORRECT IMAGE

As well as magnifying distant objects, telescopes reverse or flip the image

PAUL WHITFIELD X2, PAUL WOOTTON

WHAT TO LOOK FOR IN A REFRACTOR

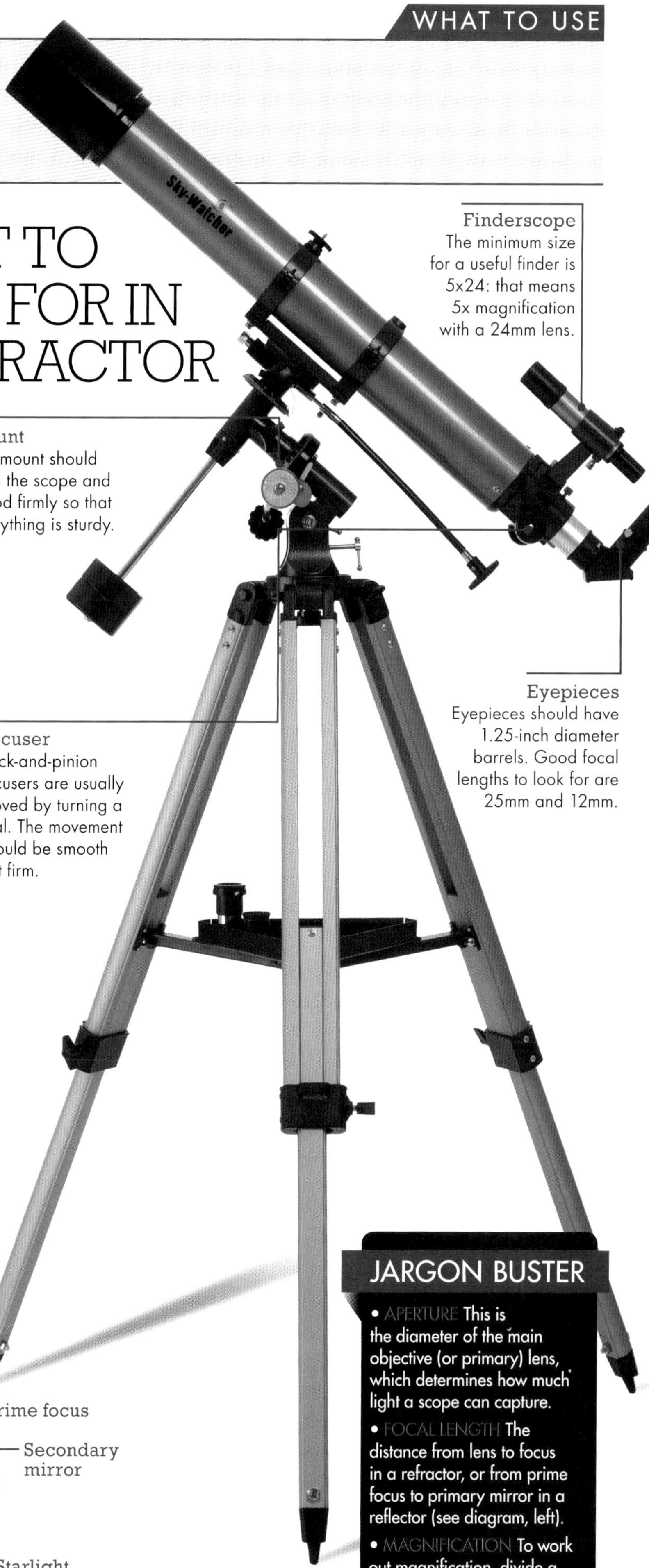

Finderscope
The minimum size for a useful finder is 5x24: that means 5x magnification with a 24mm lens.

Mount
The mount should hold the scope and tripod firmly so that everything is sturdy.

Eyepieces
Eyepieces should have 1.25-inch diameter barrels. Good focal lengths to look for are 25mm and 12mm.

Focuser
Rack-and-pinion focusers are usually moved by turning a dial. The movement should be smooth but firm.

can be magnified so we can see incredible details, such as craters on the Moon.

Whatever you do, never buy a telescope that sells itself on how much it magnifies – there are many more important things to consider. Most of the sky's fine sights can be seen with quite low magnifications, by which I mean less than 75x. Telescopes that have statements on the box like "Enter space with this 300x magnification!" should be avoided.

DECIDE ON A DIAMETER

Another critical consideration when you're deciding what to buy is the telescope's diameter. More correctly, this is called the aperture size – of the lens in the case of a refractor telescope, and of the mirror in the case of reflectors. In either case, the larger the lens or the mirror, the more light the instrument will be able to capture, and the more you can magnify.

Not surprisingly, the cost goes up as the various bits get larger. So go back to the dedicated suppliers who will consider your needs, your ability and your budget before giving you expert advice on what to buy.

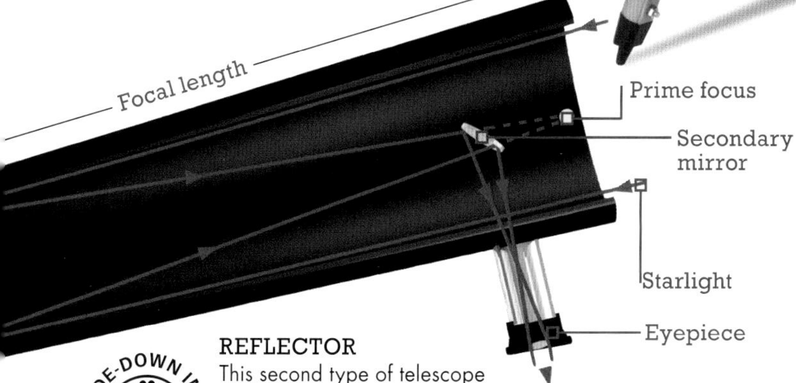

Focal length

Prime focus

Secondary mirror

Starlight

Eyepiece

UPSIDE-DOWN IMAGE

REFLECTOR
This second type of telescope captures light with a curved mirror instead of a lens. It is the mirror that does the focusing towards the secondary mirror, which deflects the light into the eyepiece.

JARGON BUSTER

• APERTURE This is the diameter of the main objective (or primary) lens, which determines how much light a scope can capture.

• FOCAL LENGTH The distance from lens to focus in a refractor, or from prime focus to primary mirror in a reflector (see diagram, left).

• MAGNIFICATION To work out magnification, divide a scope's focal length by the focal length of the eyepiece. For example, a scope with 900mm focal length and a 12.5mm eyepiece will give you 72x magnification.

COMPOUND TELESCOPES

TELESCOPES COME IN A VAST ARRAY OF SHAPES AND SIZES. HERE WE LOOK AT THE TWO COMMON VARIETIES OF CATADIOPTRIC SCOPES

NAME GAMES

The odd-sounding names for compound telescopes can tell us a lot about where their designs came from. It all started in 1672, when a French priest called Laurent Cassegrain designed a telescope with two mirrors in the arrangement we recognise today. Then in 1930, Estonian Bernhard Schmidt (pictured below) added a corrector plate at the front to create the Schmidt-Cassegrain.

The Maksutov-Cassegrain came along in 1941, thanks to the refinements of Russian astronomer Dmitri Maksutov.

Don't let anyone tell you that choosing a telescope is easy. Yes, you could just go out and buy the first instrument you see and end up with an absolutely smashing scope. Or, more likely, you could end up with one that seems too complicated, or big, or any number of other negatives.

That's not to say the telescope is always at fault. There are many people who, on a whim, go out and buy a telescope which may leave the box once; then, once the fun and excitement subsides, it ends up banished to the loft.

There are many things you can do to smooth the process: one of the best is to let those in the know (such as astronomical suppliers or societies) give you some hints and tips. But do remember that at the end of the day, it is going to be your telescope. How you wish to conduct your brand-new hobby may not be the way that experienced fellow has been conducting his observing for 30 years. Any advice you're given must be viewed in relation to what you want.

CONSIDER YOUR SITUATION

Things to consider include where you live and where you'll be observing from. Will you just need to carry the scope into the garden, or into the car

and over several hedges into a field? That could have some bearing on the size of the scope.

Other things to think about – some are obvious when you read them in black and white but can be easily overlooked – include cost, how easy it is to use and what it looks like. Does that deep green one really look better than the orange one? If you're using it as an ornament in the daytime, does it match the wallpaper? Serious decisions indeed.

The basic telescope forms (that's the reflectors and refractors) have been around for many hundreds of years, but there are newer designs that are the choice of many budding and experienced astronomers today. These are the compound or 'catadioptric' scopes. I know the name sounds like something from a hospital ER, but don't let that daunt you. If you remember, reflectors use mirrors to sort out the light and refractors use lenses. Catadioptrics use both

This Maksutov-Cassegrain is great for capturing images

HOW THEY **WORK**

These two catadioptric scopes are subtly different

Light entering a catadioptric scope first encounters a lens that sends the light down to the primary mirror. The light then bounces back up the tube to a smaller secondary mirror, or corrector plate, on the inside of the lens. This then focuses the light back down, through a hole in the primary mirror, to the eyepiece.

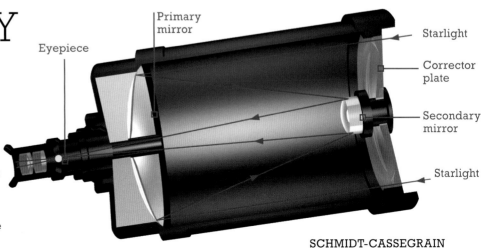

Primary mirror

Eyepiece

Starlight

Corrector plate

Secondary mirror

Starlight

SCHMIDT-CASSEGRAIN

FINDING YOUR WAY
AROUND THE SKY

Most telescopes come with a second scope: a lower magnification finder

One of the most important parts of a telescope is its finder. This little gadget with its little bolts is the key to whether you will enjoy observing or not. Finders give you a wide field view at a low magnification, which you use to line up the telescope accurately on the object in space that you wish to view. A good finder will have an objective lens above 25mm in diameter, with 5x or 6x magnification. Only the cheapest of scopes comes with no finder or too small a finder to be useful – be warned, some are as small as a miserable 10mm. For the others, it's just a matter of setting it up accurately.

You can always change a finder if it's letting you down or you're a gadget fiend – there are some brilliant laser finders around nowadays.

This Schmidt-Cassegrain has an 8x50 finder

There are many finders to choose from, such as this laser pointer

mirrors *and* lenses to do all that telescope focusing stuff. There are several designs, all with great names – there's the Schmidt-Cassegrain, the Maksutov-Cassegrain and the slightly rarer and more specialised Ritchey-Chrétien.

I say slightly more specialised, when I should say very specialised: Ritchey-Chrétien telescopes are found in professional observatories such as the Keck Telescopes on Hawaii, the Very Large Telescope in Chile and the Hubble Space Telescope. It's probably best to discount this design until you either a) own a volcano or b) have some means of putting your telescope into orbit and controlling it remotely.

So we're going for a Schmidt- or a Maksutov-Cassegrain, then. But why should this be any better than a refractor or a reflector? Well, if you're not into big telescopes then the Cassegrains are just the instrument for you. Their lens-bending, mirror-reflecting, folded light-path optics mean what would have been a rather long telescope ends up really quite neat and compact.

SCHMIDT VS MAKSUTOV

The Schmidt- and Maksutov-Cassegrain designs differ in two main areas. Firstly, the lens that lets the light in is thicker and does a slightly different job in the Maksutov, which makes it a heavier scope than the Schmidt. Secondly, because the Schmidt lens is lighter and does less of a job in bending the light, it needs a corrector plate along the light path to sort out the final image.

In other words, the Maksutov is a simpler design. Maksutovs do give very good images, but due to their heavier lenses they take longer to adjust on cold nights if you're taking them out from inside – and their field of view isn't as large as you'll get with a Schmidt. So there's really no substitute for trying out each design and seeing which one best suits your observing needs.

PROS & CONS

Pros
• Light and portable
• Great all-purpose telescopes
• Cheaper than a refractor of the same aperture
• Good for astrophotography
• Durable

Cons
• More expensive than a reflector of the same aperture
• Secondary mirror causes a slight loss of light compared to a refractor
• Will need collimating from time to time
• Images not generally as bright as other telescope types due to the number of optical elements

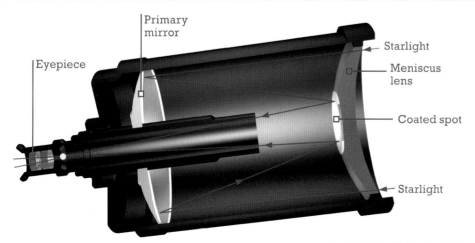

Primary mirror

Eyepiece

Starlight

Meniscus lens

Coated spot

Starlight

MAKSUTOV-CASSEGRAIN

KNOW YOUR TELESCOPE MOUNTS

A LOOK AT THAT CURIOUS STRUCTURE UNDER YOUR TELESCOPE: THE MOUNT

The first question you might ask about a telescope, if you're new to astronomy is: by how much can it magnify? The idea that you'd look at the mount to see how sturdy it is might seem absurd. It's as though the telescope is the amazing bit; the rest – the tripod that keeps the scope at the right height to look through, and the mount that fixes the scope to the tripod – is incidental.

But don't be fooled: tripods, mounts and telescopes go hand in hand. One is no good without the other two. The telescope shouldn't wobble too much, or knock you off-target when you give the mount and tripod a light tap. Generally, the cheaper the telescope the cheaper the mount, so it is always best to see any potential scope setup in the flesh to make sure that everything is good and sturdy.

The two most common types of mount are the altazimuth mount and the equatorial mount. Which one is best for you depends on what you want to do with them. Altazimuth mounts are the simplest. They move in altitude (that's up and down) and in azimuth, which is left and right. Many telescopes come with this variety of mount because they are easy to make. When it comes to observing you just plonk them on the ground and away you go.

Unsurprisingly, though, there are drawbacks to this simple solution. One is that to follow an object as it appears to move across the sky from east to west, you'll need to move your telescope in both directions at once to keep up with it: both upwards, and to the right. Another is that the view in the eyepiece rotates as the Earth turns on its axis. In other words, the orientation of the object you are looking at changes very slowly. This means that without expensive equipment, an altazimuth mount is not suited to taking astrophotos that need the camera shutter to stay open for any length of time.

THE EQUATORIAL ADVANTAGE

There are no such problems with equatorial mounts. These also have two axes of movement, but instead of an azimuth axis that's parallel to the horizon, equatorial mounts have a polar axis tilted so that it's parallel to the Earth's axis of rotation. This means that when you're setting it up, you'll need to find the latitude you're viewing from and set the polar axis to the same angle. If you don't know your latitude, you can find it from a local Ordnance Survey map, or using a website such as http://iTouchMap.com.

Before observing with an equatorial mount, you need to 'polar align' your scope. This means that the mount's polar axis, the one you aligned to your latitude, must be pointing very close to the Pole Star, so that it is aligned to the axis of Earth's rotation. You'll find the Pole Star (also called Polaris) on star charts, in the constellation Ursa Minor. Line your mount's polar scope up on the Pole Star, and then use it to align the axis to the north celestial pole. Your telescope's manual will show you how to use the polar scope.

The beauty of going through all this is that once it's done, you only need to twiddle one dial to follow the sky. Also, the view does not rotate, because the scope turns with the sky. With this type of mount, even if it's only roughly aligned, you'll be able to keep stars and other objects in view for longer, and even take pictures of the celestial bodies you're looking at.

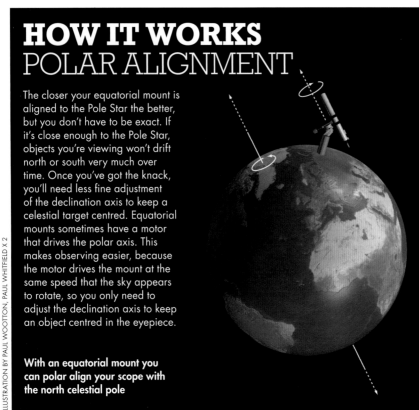

HOW IT WORKS
POLAR ALIGNMENT

The closer your equatorial mount is aligned to the Pole Star the better, but you don't have to be exact. If it's close enough to the Pole Star, objects you're viewing won't drift north or south very much over time. Once you've got the knack, you'll need less fine adjustment of the declination axis to keep a celestial target centred. Equatorial mounts sometimes have a motor that drives the polar axis. This makes observing easier, because the motor drives the mount at the same speed that the sky appears to rotate, so you only need to adjust the declination axis to keep an object centred in the eyepiece.

With an equatorial mount you can polar align your scope with the north celestial pole

TWO MOUNTS AND A TRIPOD

EQUATORIAL MOUNT
The best option to easily track an object with your telescope

Declination axis
At a right angle to the polar axis, this axis controls movement upwards and downwards in the sky. Use it to find objects you want to look at.

Mounting plate
This strong metal plate attaches the telescope to the mount. Depending on the telescope, this may feature a set of rings that attach around the entire tube.

Polar scope
This is a small, built-in telescope that's parallel to the polar axis. Look through it to help you align the main scope with Earth's axis of rotation.

Polar axis
By tilting this axis to the same angle as your latitude and pointing it close to the Pole Star, it will sit roughly parallel to Earth's axis. This enables you to keep moving targets in view.

Tripod
This raises the scope and mount off the ground to give you as comfortable an observing height as possible. It also makes the scope sturdy, so that it doesn't wobble and ruin the view.

ALTAZIMUTH MOUNT
The simple mount many telescopes are sold with

A basic telescope mount that moves both left and right (azimuth), and up and down (altitude).

PHOTOGRAPHIC TRIPOD
A budget solution that's strictly for beginners

You can mount a small refractor telescope on a simple photographic tripod, if you have one. It's not perfect but it does offer a quick way to start observing.

EQUATORIAL MOUNTS

PART 1 SETTING UP

EQUATORIAL MOUNTS LET YOU TRACK AN OBJECT AS IT MOVES ACROSS THE NIGHT SKY

Putting your telescope on an equatorial mount enables you to follow stars as they continue their steady progress across the night sky. The mount may look complex, but it really doesn't take long to master.

Over the next six pages, we're breaking down everything about these mounts into easy-to-follow steps, starting with putting them together. We're using an EQ3 mount, but the techniques will work for other types, too.

MOUNT HEAD

An equatorial mount is made up of a tripod and a mount head, which holds the telescope and moves it about on two axes, one called right ascension (RA) and the other called declination (Dec.)

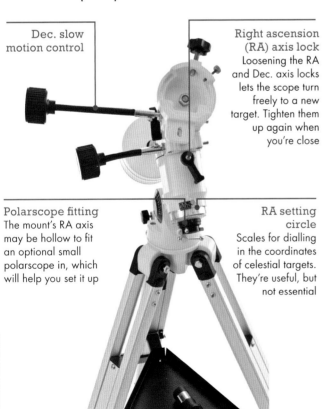

Dec. slow motion control

Right ascension (RA) axis lock
Loosening the RA and Dec. axis locks lets the scope turn freely to a new target. Tighten them up again when you're close

Polarscope fitting
The mount's RA axis may be hollow to fit an optional small polarscope in, which will help you set it up

RA setting circle
Scales for dialling in the coordinates of celestial targets. They're useful, but not essential

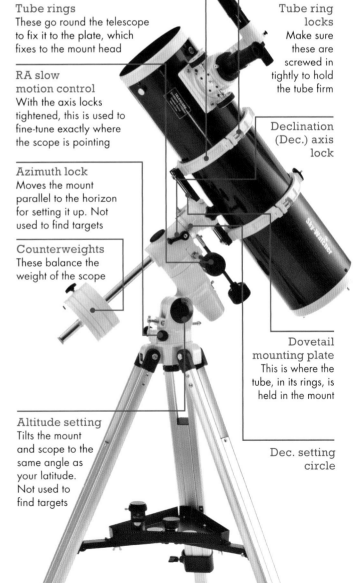

Tube rings
These go round the telescope to fix it to the plate, which fixes to the mount head

Tube ring locks
Make sure these are screwed in tightly to hold the tube firm

RA slow motion control
With the axis locks tightened, this is used to fine-tune exactly where the scope is pointing

Azimuth lock
Moves the mount parallel to the horizon for setting it up. Not used to find targets

Counterweights
These balance the weight of the scope

Declination (Dec.) axis lock

Dovetail mounting plate
This is where the tube, in its rings, is held in the mount

Altitude setting
Tilts the mount and scope to the same angle as your latitude. Not used to find targets

Dec. setting circle

HOW TO ASSEMBLE YOUR MOUNT

Follow these steps to make sure your equatorial mount is solidly built and won't collapse when you fit your telescope onto it

1. The scope and mount head sit on a **TRIPOD**. Set this up in daylight if it's your first time. Adjust the height of the tripod's legs so the top is level with your hips and, if there is one, fit the central accessory tray. Make sure that the top is level and that the leg labelled 'N' is pointing north.

2. Place the **MOUNT HEAD** onto the top of the tripod. Line up the metal peg on the top of the tripod with the gap underneath the mount, between the azimuth lock's two bolts. Secure the mount head onto the tripod by tightening the big bolt hanging from the underside of the tripod top.

3. Screw the **COUNTERWEIGHT** bar into the mount head. With the rod's locknut tightened against the mount, take the safety screw off the end of the bar and slide the counterweights halfway up the bar, tightening the screws on the weights to secure them. Then replace the safety screw on the end.

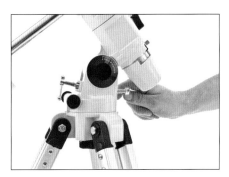

4. The RA axis needs to point up to the north celestial pole. To do this, the mount's **ALTITUDE SETTING** needs to be the same as your local latitude. Release the front and back bolts and tilt the mount head so that the pointer lines up with the right number on the altitude scale, then do the bolts up again.

5. Fit a **SLOW MOTION CABLE** onto the small D-shaped shafts on the RA and the Dec. axes, tightening the screw at the end of each cable to hold it in place. If using a refractor, rotate the Dec. axis so that the cable extends to the bottom. For a reflector, fix the cable on at the top, closest to the eyepiece.

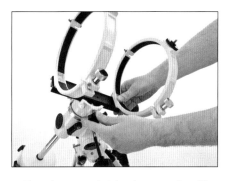

6. The telescope is held in the mount head by two **TUBE RINGS**, which are attached to a mounting plate clamped tightly into the mount head. Our example has a short dovetail mounting plate with two tube rings already attached, but yours may not be fixed to the mount head. In which case, attach the rings.

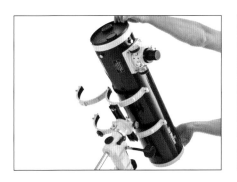

7. With the tube rings open, **PLACE THE TUBE IN THE RINGS**, then flip the top half of the rings over the tube and screw down the locking bolts tightly so the tube doesn't slide out. You might need an extra pair of hands to help you at this point. Remember, if you've got a reflector the eyepiece goes at the top!

8. Slip the **FINDERSCOPE** into its bracket and screw this into the clamp on the telescope tube. To align it, put a low-mag eyepiece in the main scope's focuser and find something like a pylon on the horizon. Then look through the finderscope and adjust the screws on its bracket until the pylon is in its crosshairs.

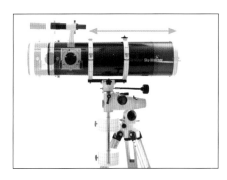

9. BALANCE YOUR SCOPE. With the tube horizontal and the Dec. axis lock loose, slide the tube back and forth in the rings until the scope rests flat. Then do the RA axis: with the counterweight shaft horizontal, loosen the lock and adjust the counterweights until the scope stays put when you let go.

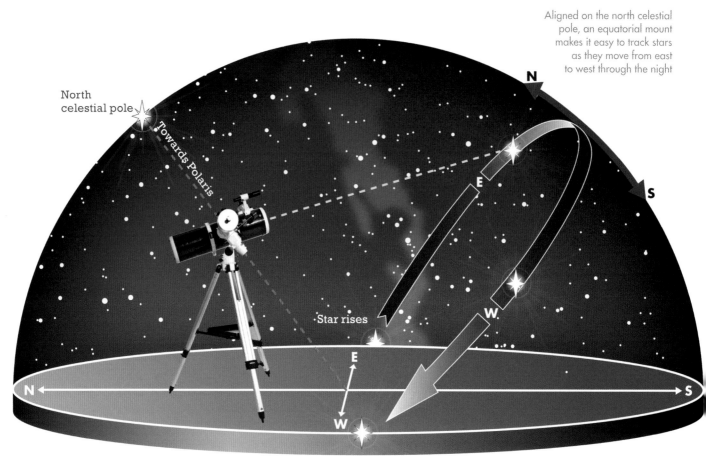

North celestial pole

Towards Polaris

N

N

S

E

W

Star rises

E

W

N

S

Star sets

EQUATORIAL MOUNTS

PART 2 ALIGNING

THE SECOND PART OF OUR GUIDE TO EQUATORIAL MOUNTS SHOWS YOU HOW TO ALIGN ONE SO THAT IT CAN TRACK THE STARS

STEVE MARSH, PAUL WHITFIELD X 4

In Part 1, we looked at setting up an equatorial mount so it would be a solid and stable platform for holding your telescope. Now we're going to explain how to make the mount follow, or track, stars and other objects as they move with the sky as the night hours tick by.

To do this properly, the equatorial mount has to be 'polar aligned'; its right ascension (RA) or polar axis must be lined up so that it points at the north celestial pole. This is the point that the sky appears to rotate around.

It's a notional spot that denotes the point at which our planet's axis of rotation meets celestial sphere, that imaginary ball with the Earth at its centre, onto whose inner surface all the stars are projected. The sky, in fact, only appears to rotate; it's actually Earth that's rotating, once every 24 hours. But since we're observing from the surface of the spinning Earth, it looks as though it's the night sky that is rotating around us.

Since the sky rotates (or appears to) around the north celestial pole, the mount

ALIGNMENT TIME

Four steps to getting your scope lined up on the north celestial pole

STEP 1 Adjust the mount's altitude setting so that it's the same as your local latitude. In the UK, this will be between 58° (John O'Groats) and 50° (Land's End). Release the front and back bolts and tilt the mount head so that the pointer lines up with the right number on the altitude scale, then do the bolts up again. Doing this aligns the mount's right ascension (RA) or polar axis with the Earth's axis of rotation, so that the two are parallel.

STEP 2 As well as being angled up, the polar axis needs to be aimed so its highest end points due north. Some mounts have a big 'N' at the top of the tripod to show which side should face north. You can use a compass to find out which direction is north, but remember that this will show magnetic north and we want true north, which is a few degrees east. At night, find the star Polaris and line up the polar axis with it.

STEP 3 The mount should now be polar aligned. To check that it is, when the stars are out look along the polar axis up at the sky and make sure that it is pointing at the star Polaris. This kind of visual alignment is fine for making observations through the eyepiece. But for more accuracy – if you want to take photos through your scope, for instance – you'll need to polar align looking up through a polarscope fitted in the RA axis.

STEP 4 If you need to make any fine adjustments to get the polar axis aimed at the north celestial pole, use the altitude and azimuth settings. Make altitude adjustments like those covered in step 1. To make azimuth adjustments, unscrew the two azimuth bolts to move the mount head and scope left or right slightly, parallel to the horizon. This is easier than lifting the tripod and the whole setup to aim the scope due north.

THE POLE STAR

In the northern hemisphere, we're lucky enough to have a fairly bright star sitting practically at the point that the sky appears to rotate around: the north celestial pole. This star is Polaris, the Pole Star, in Ursa Minor. Find it and you'll have found true north. What's more, it never shifts from that position during the night while everything else in the sky turns around it.

Polaris is actually 0.7° away from the north celestial pole. This tiny offset doesn't matter for visual observations, but to take astro images you'll need more accuracy: polar aligning through a polarscope takes that 0.7° offset into account. Polaris is easy to find, courtesy of two stars in Ursa Major known as the Pointers. Simply draw a line through them and you'll end up at Polaris, as shown below.

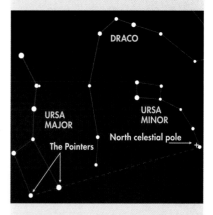

Find Polaris by drawing a line to it through the two stars in Ursa Major known as the Pointers (see page 15)

also has to be aligned to this axis of rotation to track the stars' movement. Equatorial mounts are designed specifically to be polar aligned – if you don't bother, you might as well have saved your money and bought a cheaper altazimuth mount.

POLE POSITION

When it comes to getting your mount's polar axis pointing in the right direction, those of us in the northern hemisphere have a helping hand because the bright star Polaris sits very

close to the celestial pole. This provides an instant 'marker' – and the good news is that for visual observations, you don't even need to be overly accurate in your polar alignment. It's simply a case of adjusting the altitude setting so it's the same as your local latitude (find this at http://itouchmap.com/latlong. html), then pointing the polar axis north so it's lined up on Polaris. If you're intending to do any astrophotography, though, then you'll need to be more accurate, and you should polar align using the mount's polarscope.

Once the mount has been lined up on the celestial pole, your scope will track the stars with ease and you'll find it simple to keep objects in your eyepiece for longer. You only need to adjust the RA or polar axis with its slow-motion control to do this. It's unlike a camera-type altazimuth mount, which needs its two axes to be adjusted to track objects. But remember that even an equatorial mount will need both its axes adjusted when you want to move the scope so that it points at another star.

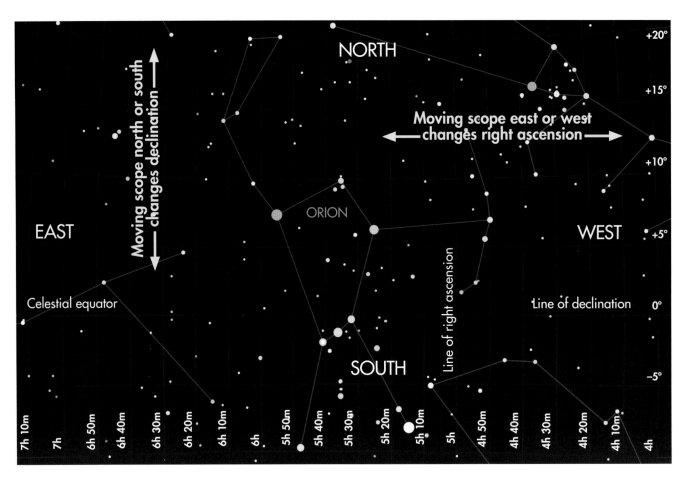

Chart labels:
- NORTH
- +20°
- +15°
- +10°
- Moving scope east or west changes right ascension
- Moving scope north or south changes declination
- ORION
- EAST
- WEST
- +5°
- Line of right ascension
- Celestial equator
- Line of declination
- 0°
- SOUTH
- −5°
- 7h 10m, 7h, 6h 50m, 6h 40m, 6h 30m, 6h 20m, 6h 10m, 6h, 5h 50m, 5h 40m, 5h 30m, 5h 20m, 5h 10m, 5h, 4h 50m, 4h 40m, 4h 30m, 4h 20m, 4h 10m, 4h

EQUATORIAL MOUNTS

PART 3 HOW THE MOUNT MOVES

HOW TO MOVE AN EQUATORIAL MOUNT'S AXES TO KEEP YOU ON TARGET

CHART BY PETE LAWRENCE, PAUL WHITFIELD X 5

In the first two parts of this guide to equatorial amounts, we've looked at how to set up your mount so that it will do its job properly, making it easy to find and follow objects out there in space. A star, planet or nebula can be found by using its co-ordinates on the great imaginary sphere projected onto the night sky, with the Earth at its centre – the celestial sphere.

As we mentioned previously, finding a galaxy in this way is almost identical to the way you locate places on Earth using latitude and longitude; you just imagine the grid projected onto the starry realm. The only difference is that on the celestial sphere,

latitude is known as declination (or Dec. for short) and longitude is known as right ascension (or simply RA).

Both of these systems work in exactly the same way as they do for locations on Earth. Declination (latitude) lines run parallel to the equator from east to west, while right ascension (longitude) lines run 'up and down', from north to south. Every single object in the night sky has Dec. and RA co-ordinates, just as every location on earth has a latitude and a longitude. By using the Dec. and RA setting circles on your equatorial mount, you can point your scope to find anything in the sky with just these two figures.

WHEN THE TUBE BUMPS THE TRIPOD

To keep track of your quarry as it moves from east to west, you might need to do a 'meridian flip'

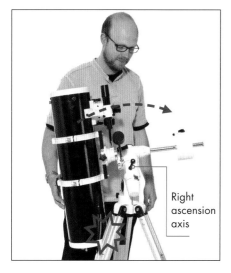

Declination axis

Right ascension axis

STEP 1 If your telescope's tube bumps into the tripod as you're tracking an object moving with the night sky, rotate the telescope tube by 180° in right ascension.

STEP 2 Next, rotate the declination axis so that the telescope tube is pointing at the object again. You can use the declination axis setting circle to get back to the original spot.

STEP 3 You're ready to begin observing again. A meridian flip is often needed on objects that are at their highest in the sky, so the tube is pointing straight up.

Assuming you've already polar aligned your scope as detailed in Part 2, the first step to finding that galaxy is to make sure your right ascension setting circle is set correctly. For this you'll need the RA co-ordinates of an easily found bright star, like Vega in the constellation of Lyra (see page 10). Vega's co-ordinates can be found from a star atlas, or a planetarium program like Stellarium.

HEAD FOR VEGA

Loosen the locks on both the RA and Dec. axes and move the scope until it is more or less visually aligned with the star, then use the slow-motion controls – and your finderscope – to zero in on the target. Now take a look at the RA setting circle dial. If this is your first setup, it might not be reading the exact RA position that you looked up earlier.

If this is the case, don't worry: simply rotate the RA setting circle's dial until the pointer reads the correct co-ordinate. The Dec. setting circle's dial is fixed in the correct position, so you needn't fret about this going out of alignment. Now you can use the setting circles to find your galaxy, simply by moving the axes so that the setting circles match the galaxy's Dec. and RA co-ordinates. You can use this method to locate objects that are below naked eye visibility, too.

The beauty of the equatorial mount now comes into play: as you gaze in wonderment at your galaxy, you only need to adjust the RA axis with its slow-motion control to keep it in your eyepiece as it moves from east to west across the sky. And if you find the occasional twiddling of the RA slow-motion control a little tedious, you can get a motor to attach to this axis, which will do the tracking for you automatically. As for the declination axis, you don't have to touch that or its slow-motion control until you want to look at a different object. Then you just look up the co-ordinates of your next quarry, and move the Dec. axis and the RA axis until the setting circle dials give the right readings.

So, a well-handled equatorial mount is pretty much the perfect solution to hassle-free stargazing. Well, almost; there is one thing it can't do, and that's track an object all the way across the sky. There will come a point when the bottom of the scope's tube will bump into the tripod leg, especially if it's a long tube. Luckily, there's an easy way around this called a 'meridian flip' – see above.

Hopefully, if you've read all three parts of this article, you've now got a bit more confidence when it comes to using an equatorial mount. Astronomers have been fixing their telescopes on this kind of mount for almost two centuries; now you can too.

Adjusting the declination axis moves your telescope in a north-south direction

Adjusting the right ascension axis moves your telescope in an east-west direction

GO-TO TELESCOPES

LOCATE CELESTIAL OBJECTS AT THE PUSH OF A BUTTON WITH OUR GUIDE TO USING A GO-TO TELESCOPE

To get an idea of just how much modern technology has influenced astronomical observing, take a look at the Go-To scope. A Go-To is basically an ordinary telescope, but added to its mount are motors and a digital map of the night sky containing tens of thousands of astronomical objects. All this is stored in computer circuitry within the mount and it's this, rather than the scope itself, that is really the 'Go-To' part of the system.

Once the Go-To has been correctly set up, you simply choose a celestial object that you want to view by using the buttons on the handset. It's at this point the motors kick in and the whole mechanism whirs and turns around, 'going to' the object you've chosen, which will eventually appear in the eyepiece. Pretty straightforward, don't you think?

Certainly, but there's a reason why Go-To telescopes come with such a substantial manual. Before you can get to the impressive stage of being driven around the sky to objects you've selected, you first need to have your Go-To scope set up correctly. Using a Go-To is not the straight-out-of-the-box method of stargazing it might at first appear.

SETTING UP

There are a few things you need to know in order to get a Go-To scope working. Firstly, not every scope has the same set-up routine, nor are these routines all as easy to perform as each other. When deciding on a Go-To scope, you should do plenty of research to avoid buying one that you'll never use because it's too complicated.

There's some basic information that the Go-To computer needs to know when you're

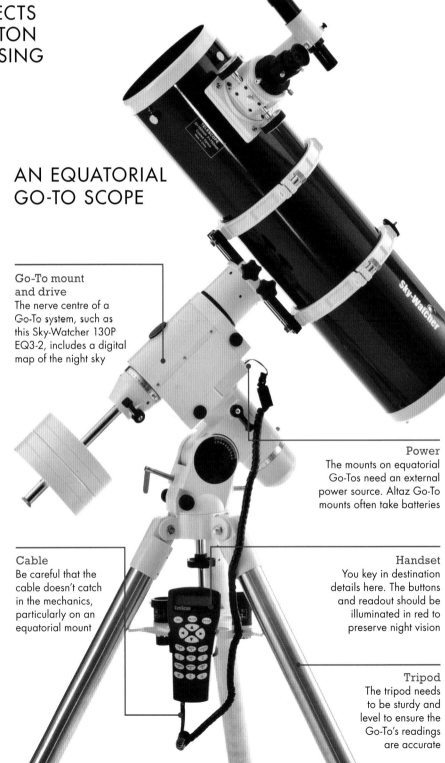

AN EQUATORIAL GO-TO SCOPE

Go-To mount and drive
The nerve centre of a Go-To system, such as this Sky-Watcher 130P EQ3-2, includes a digital map of the night sky

Power
The mounts on equatorial Go-Tos need an external power source. Altaz Go-To mounts often take batteries

Handset
You key in destination details here. The buttons and readout should be illuminated in red to preserve night vision

Cable
Be careful that the cable doesn't catch in the mechanics, particularly on an equatorial mount

Tripod
The tripod needs to be sturdy and level to ensure the Go-To's readings are accurate

LATITUDE
AND LONGITUDE

If you live in a small town or a rural environment, the computer database in the Go-To handset may not have location details for your area. In this case you'll need to supply the co-ordinates of your latitude and longitude. There are plenty of websites that make it easy to discover these location details. They often feature a world map so you can zoom in and click on your location to find your co-ordinates.

You may need to convert the latitude and longitude of your location from the decimal version into hours, minutes and seconds. A search online for 'latitude longitude conversion' will bring up myriad sites that will do this.

Only use the minus sign for latitude if you are south of the equator, as it means the southern hemisphere. For longitude, minus means that the location is west of the Greenwich Meridian, pictured left, so this includes all of western Britain, North and South America. Parts of Britain east of Greenwich, and all of Europe and Australia, have a positive longitude. Not that these locations need a plus sign.

Some Go-To scopes, such as the Meade ETX 90PE, sit on altaz mounts

setting it up: your location, the date and the time. With these details keyed in to the Go-To, the telescope can correctly orientate the star charts in its memory. Some Go-To scopes come with a GPS receiver built-in that helps with this initiation procedure.

Now you're ready for alignment. Firstly, make sure the tripod and telescope are level. If there's any sloping ground you haven't compensated for, the scope will miss its target object. This is especially true for a Go-To on an equatorial mount, such as the Sky-Watcher Explorer 150P. With scopes like these, you should polar align the mount first. The Go-To system will then ask you to centre several alignment stars in the eyepiece. When you've done this, you're ready to go.

Other Go-To scopes, such as the Meade ETX 90PE, are mounted on an altazimuth mount – either a single-arm or fork type. With an altaz mount, you will need to centre one or two alignment stars in the view. With either equatorial or altaz Go-Tos, the more stars you align on, the more accurate the mount will be. This is a consideration that becomes particularly important if you're planning to do any astrophotography.

Finally, remember that there's one essential link in this high-tech chain of technology – batteries. Always carry spares, or consider buying a powerpack to ensure you don't run out of power while observing.

THE PROS & CONS

Pros
- In light-polluted skies, it's easier to locate objects that you wouldn't otherwise be able to find if you were manually star-hopping when the stars might be washed out.
- Go-Tos are good for taking photos that are free of star trails, as the scope will track the movement of the night sky.
- If you're planning to show friends several objects in the night sky, a Go-To is fast and efficient.
- A Go-To database can be updated when new comets or supernovae are discovered, so you can find new objects quickly and easily.

Cons
- The database may contain tens of thousands of objects, but how many you can see will also depend on the scope's optics and seeing conditions.
- You need to ensure the battery has enough charge for the observing session – once a Go-To scope has lost its power there is no way to use it manually.
- By not manually scanning the heavens, and with the scope doing all the locating, you may miss chance encounters with intriguing objects.
- You need to set up and align a Go-To correctly each time you head out to observe, in order for it to accurately locate objects. This takes time.

INTRODUCTION TO EYEPIECES

EYEPIECES MAY BE SMALL, BUT THEY PLAY A BIG ROLE WHEN IT COMES TO ENSURING YOU GET THE MOST FROM YOUR OBSERVING SESSIONS

COATINGS

As light passes through the lenses in your eyepiece, a little bit of it is taken away. To minimise this loss of light, manufacturers coat the lenses with substances like magnesium or calcium fluoride. The best eyepieces will be the ones that say they are 'fully multi-coated', though 'multi-coated' eyepieces are still good. Try to avoid eyepieces that are described as 'fully coated' or just 'coated'. One way to test the coatings is to fix a black cap on the bottom of your eyepiece and look down the barrel in daylight. The darker the glass looks, the less light is lost and the better the eyepiece.

The importance of eyepieces took me a long time to realise. To say they can make or break you as an amateur astronomer may be going a little too far, but certainly when you look through a good eyepiece you realise that what you've been observing for all those years could have looked much clearer. It all comes down to experience. In fact, I'm glad I went through the 'fuzzy faint years', as I call them, because I now appreciate what it takes to see the sky properly.

The reason my observations were so limited was that I had been bought a small refracting telescope for Christmas when I was 10 years old. It had a metal tripod, a basic altazimuth mount, a finder, eyepieces and a Barlow lens that doubled their magnification. Needless to say, I had many, many observing sessions with that first telescope and its eyepieces.

The mount came with an eyepiece tray that sat between the tripod legs and held the Barlow lens – always a useful feature when observing. As all eyepieces are a slightly different length depending on their power, it was quite easy to feel which was which in the dark when I wanted to change the view. And I took great care of those rather poor

HOW AN EYEPIECE WORKS

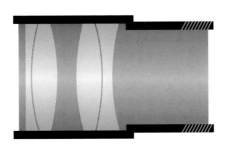

PLÖSSL EYEPIECE

Of the 25 or so types of eyepiece around, this is the one you will mostly hear about as it's the most common. The internal construction of two back-to-back convex and concave lenses, and the quality needed for the lens elements, makes them fairly costly to make and buy. Plössls benefit from a wide field of view (around 52°), but eye relief can be a bit short if the lens has a focal length of 12mm or less.

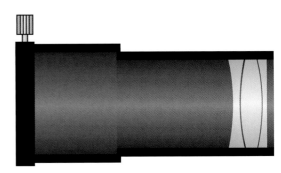

BARLOW LENS

This is not so much an eyepiece, but an eyepiece's friend. A Barlow lens intercepts the light from the telescope before giving it to an eyepiece. What this lens does is double or triple the magnification you would otherwise get from just an eyepiece alone. So, buy your eyepieces carefully and let a single well-made Barlow effectively double the number of eyepieces, and therefore powers, you have.

An eyepiece sits in a telescope's focuser, held there tightly by a little screw

eyepieces. Like most that come with small, child-friendly refractors, or indeed reflectors, they were not of the greatest quality. But nevertheless, I used to put them back into their little boxes after every observing session and I made sure they stayed scrupulously clean. If I hadn't, perhaps I'd have had to replace them sooner – and so would have realised earlier how much I was missing!

At least I got into good habits, though. I still take care of my eyepieces: the last thing you want to do with these seemingly insignificant, yet important, things that you pop into the end of your telescope is to get them scratched or damaged.

That's because an eyepiece is just as important as the scope's main lens or mirror. It takes the light that's captured and focused by the scope and magnifies the image that goes into your eye. It sounds simple, but the eyepiece needs to do this effectively if you're to get a really good view.

COST AND QUALITY

Another reason to keep your eyepieces in the best possible condition – and possibly one reason why they are not always a major consideration when you're buying observing equipment – is the cost of replacing them. The better little cylindrical eyepieces are manufactured to an exceptionally high standard. Some have multiple glass lenses inside that fit together to give you a beautifully crafted accessory that will last and last. You can pay anything from around £30 up to £400 for a good eyepiece – and an item with that kind of price tag is something you'll definitely want to look after.

The diameter of an eyepiece gives some indication of how well it's built. If the barrel measures just under an inch in diameter (and most eyepieces are described in imperial units) then it's most likely been given away with one of the cheaper telescopes. But in truth, neither the telescope nor the eyepiece will be with you for the long-term. Most decent telescopes for beginners have a 1.25-inch eyepiece barrel; when you get up to the really good stuff, though, it's two inches all the way.

ULTRA-WIDE ANGLE

As the name suggests, this provides you with an ultra-wide 82° or so field of view, which is just gigantic. There is also a super-wide angle version with a 67° field of view, but the scene through an ultra is something else. If you took one apart (though this is certainly not recommended) you would find six or seven elements, all coated to provide you with the best light-gathering possible.

CHOOSING AN EYEPIECE

MAKE SURE YOU GET THE BEST VIEW OF THE NIGHT SKY BY USING THE RIGHT EYEPIECE

Which is more important: the telescope or the eyepiece? The telescope gets lots of attention because it's the most expensive and impressive-looking part of your setup – but without decent eyepieces, the views you get can be disappointing.

What you ideally want is a good range of eyepieces, because different sizes of focal length are useful in producing better views of different kinds of objects. This is due to the fact that each eyepiece will have a differing field of view and magnification, depending on the telescope used.

To find out what magnification you're getting with any eyepiece takes a very easy calculation – you simply divide the focal length of the telescope, which is usually printed on a label on the scope near the eyepiece end, by the focal length of the eyepiece. The focal length of any decent eyepiece will be marked in millimetres around its collar. So for example, to work out the magnification of an 800mm focal length telescope with a standard 25mm focal length eyepiece, you divide 800 by 25, which is 32. This setup will magnify objects you see in the eyepiece by a factor of 32.

For wider views of nebulae and star clusters, this is the kind of number you will want. With higher magnifications, maybe with a 10mm eyepiece, you'll get more detailed views of the planets and double stars.

As you progress in astronomy, you will undoubtedly start to experiment with the different views that a range of eyepieces can offer. So make sure you don't underestimate these small, seemingly insignificant bits of astro equipment!

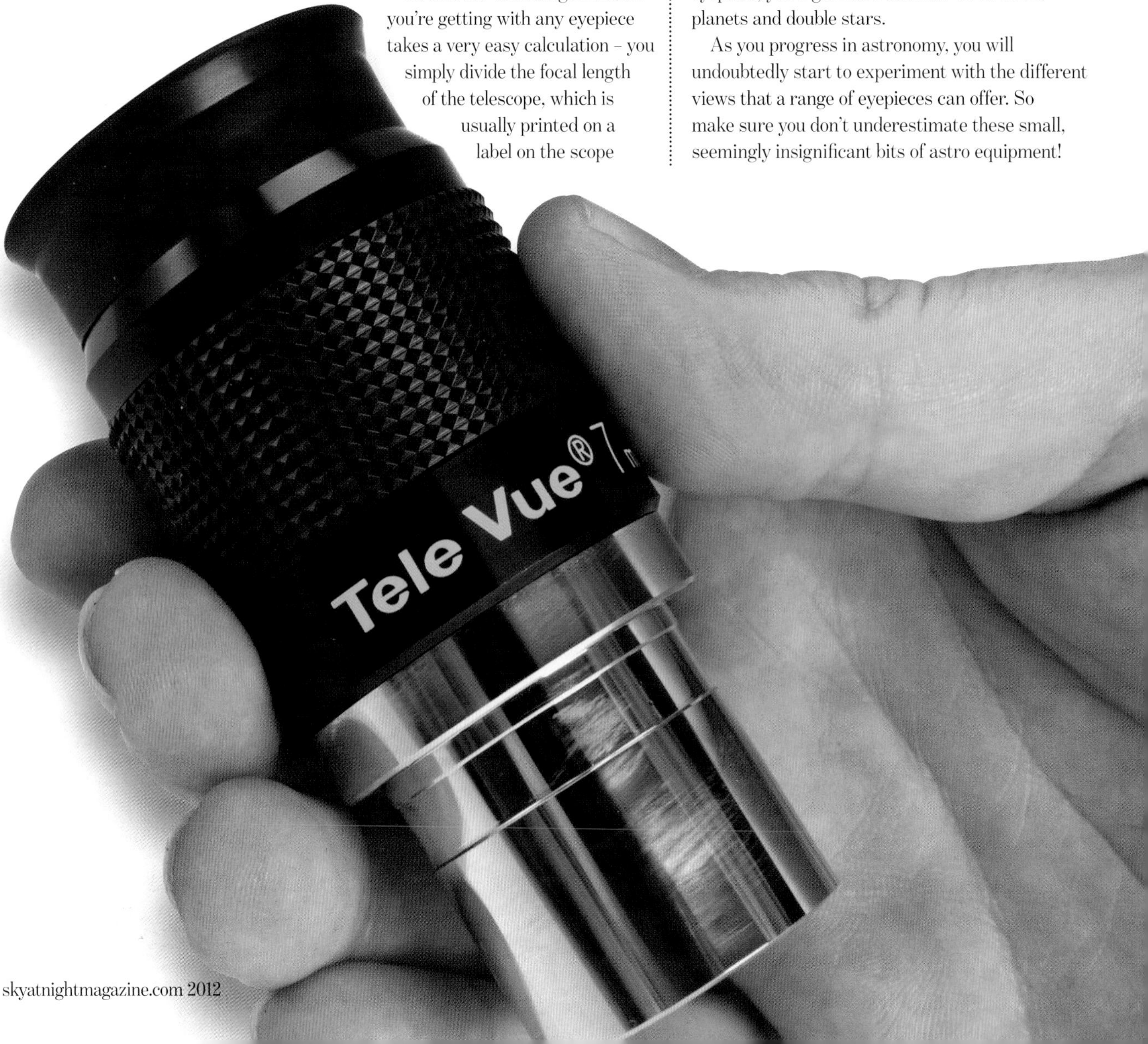

PAUL WHITFIELD X 4, STUIDO4PHOTO, TELE VUE, WILL GATER

KNOW YOUR EYEPIECES

There are four main types of eyepiece. Adding a Barlow lens will increase their magnification

PLÖSSL
From £20 to £150

Plössls have a wide field of view (around 52°), so they can be used successfully for planetary as well as deep-sky viewing. The only drawback is the short eye relief that becomes an issue with focal lengths of 12mm or less. Eye relief refers to how far your eye must be from the eyepiece in order for you to see the entire field of view.

The internal construction of a Plössl eyepiece consists of two back-to-back lens systems. There's quite a price variation between the highest quality examples and those produced more cheaply.

RADIAN
Around £180

The Radian is one of the newer types of eyepiece on the market. With a field of view comparable to a Plössl, you may wonder what the difference is? Well, one is the big eye relief – even with focal lengths down to 3mm. This is a lifesaver if you need to wear glasses while observing, and very user-friendly for everyone else. The design suits medium and higher magnifications in order to get plenty of detail when looking at the planets. Internally, there are six or seven lens elements that have very short focal lengths.

NAGLER
From £170 to £440

The Nagler's most impressive attribute is its huge field of view. While other manufacturers keep their eyepieces within the human eye's 50° field of view, Naglers go the extra mile to develop an ultra-wide 82° field. Imagine the amazing vistas of star fields and nebulae you get with that! The design incorporates six or seven elements, all coated with special chemicals to increase the amount of light that travels through the eyepiece. The downside to some of these eyepieces is their weight, which may require you to rebalance your scope.

ORTHOSCOPIC
From £30 to £75

These were the mainstay for many an amateur astronomer until the Plössls took over, but Orthoscopics are still good little eyepieces. They're made with a four-element optical system that provides very good eye relief. The design also keeps down the amount of light that is refracted within the system very effectively.

The field of view, at only 40° to 45°, may not be as great as a Plössl, but they are still pretty good all-rounders. They come in particularly useful for making observations of the Moon and planets.

DOUBLE UP WITH A BARLOW LENS

This is a marvellous bit of kit. It isn't actually an eyepiece, but has optical elements that work with an eyepiece to increase the magnification. This is achieved by a very simple process: you basically slot the eyepiece into the Barlow lens and the whole contraption gets popped into where the eyepiece would normally go. Depending on the Barlow, you can double or triple the magnification you would get from the eyepiece alone. This means that with one Barlow lens you have effectively doubled the number of eyepieces – and therefore magnifications – that you have at your disposal.

FIELD OF VIEW

These three diagrams show what field of view (FOV) is all about. Needless to say, the wider the field of view, the more of the sky you can see. The first view of the Moon shown here is that seen using just a 25mm eyepiece. In the next image we take an even closer look, with a narrower field of view, by changing to a 10mm eyepiece. Finally, an even smaller field of view as we use a Barlow lens with the 10mm eyepiece. The FOV is given in degrees (°) and arcminutes (') above each view.

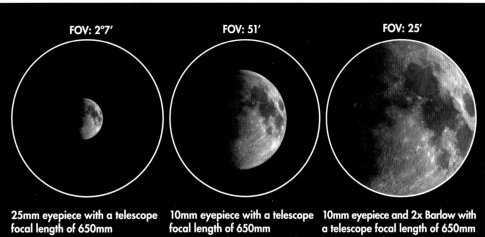

FOV: 2°7'
25mm eyepiece with a telescope focal length of 650mm

FOV: 51'
10mm eyepiece with a telescope focal length of 650mm

FOV: 25'
10mm eyepiece and 2x Barlow with a telescope focal length of 650mm

FILTERS

THESE LITTLE ACCESSORIES CAN HELP YOU CUT DOWN ON MOON GLARE AND EASE THE WOE OF OBSERVING FROM LIGHT-POLLUTED AREAS

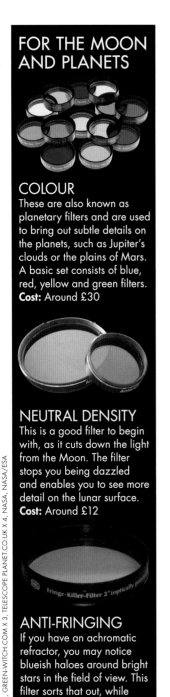

FOR THE MOON AND PLANETS

COLOUR
These are also known as planetary filters and are used to bring out subtle details on the planets, such as Jupiter's clouds or the plains of Mars. A basic set consists of blue, red, yellow and green filters.
Cost: Around £30

NEUTRAL DENSITY
This is a good filter to begin with, as it cuts down the light from the Moon. The filter stops you being dazzled and enables you to see more detail on the lunar surface.
Cost: Around £12

ANTI-FRINGING
If you have an achromatic refractor, you may notice blueish haloes around bright stars in the field of view. This filter sorts that out, while also helping to make planets appear a little more crisp.
Cost: Around £45

You can think of these small telescope accessories as sunglasses for your scope. They work in a similar way, too. Imagine a day with the Sun shining in a clear blue sky. As you put on your shades the resulting scene becomes dimmed as the lenses stop some of the light from getting into your eyes. This 'stopping' is actually a filtering out of some of the sunlight and this effect enables you to look at things more clearly.

LESS IS MORE
Filters for telescopes do exactly the same thing: they take away, or filter out, some aspect of light heading down into your telescope, so you're better able to view starry objects. It's quite strange to think that by removing light you can see better, especially when it comes to space views. We're always told to make sure we get as much star light as possible to the eye, but at times less really does mean more. And that's the point of telescope filters: to remove unwanted light and thus bring out or emphasise the object – be it a nebula or a lunar crater – that you want to see.

The sheer variety of telescope filters that are available is incredible, and this can be quite bewildering for beginners. Some are coloured, some block certain types of light, some are very cheap at just a few pounds, while others are expensive, costing hundreds of pounds. The filter you should buy depends upon your viewing conditions, the object you're looking at and what details you actually want to see. There are different filters for the different types of objects up there: the Sun, the Moon, planets, stars, nebulae and galaxies.

Some of you might have used filters in photography before, and so may have some idea of what to expect. However, it's worth taking a little time to understand what's happening to the light when it travels through each filter, and what is the best use of a filter for a particular object.

Some filters can appear to be nothing more than innocent-looking round bits of coloured glass from a church window. However, there's a difference.

Filters help cut out light from bright objects such as the Moon

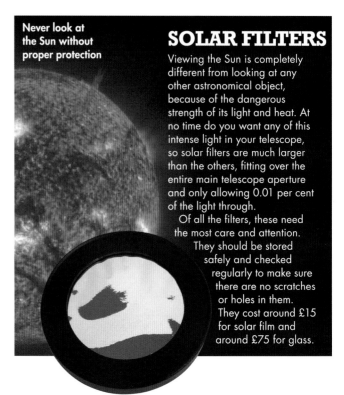

Never look at the Sun without proper protection

SOLAR FILTERS
Viewing the Sun is completely different from looking at any other astronomical object, because of the dangerous strength of its light and heat. At no time do you want any of this intense light in your telescope, so solar filters are much larger than the others, fitting over the entire main telescope aperture and only allowing 0.01 per cent of the light through.

Of all the filters, these need the most care and attention. They should be stored safely and checked regularly to make sure there are no scratches or holes in them. They cost around £15 for solar film and around £75 for glass.

BROADBAND
Also known as light-pollution reduction filters. By filtering out the light from certain types of street lamp they darken the sky, allowing nebulae, comets, galaxies and star clusters to stand out. **Cost:** From £45

NARROWBAND
These filters for nebulae are designed to let through light from glowing hydrogen or oxygen from the nebulae, while eliminating sky glow and street lamp pollution. **Cost:** From £70

ULTRA-HIGH CONTRAST
These filters are for serious nebula observers who have a good scope and dark skies. They let in only very selective light from these clouds and have various coatings to blacken the sky. **Cost:** From £75

The difference is that these particular bits of glass are contained in a metal frame, which has a screw thread. You use this to screw the filter onto the back of your eyepiece before you pop it into your telescope. This is where filters go, as a rule – all except solar filters, which for reasons that are explained on the opposite page, fit onto your telescope's front lens.

FILTER SELECTION
It can be quite easy to forget when you've put a filter on because, once the eyepiece is in the telescope, the filter is out of view. Many times, even experienced observers have scratched their heads because the telescope view was not as they expected, only to eventually find a filter left lurking on the eyepiece. You can actually get adventurous and combine filters, but it's not recommended to use more than two at a time because light loss becomes a problem.

Perhaps the easiest filter to begin with is the kind known as a neutral density filter, which is a lot like the sunglasses we've talked about. This dims the view of all colours from entering your eye and is great for cutting down on the bright light from the Moon, especially around the time of its full phase. There are, however, many other kinds of filters and we've listed a selection on these pages.

Happy filtering!

The Hubble Space Telescope employs sophisticated filters

FILTERS IN SPACE

All the filters mentioned here are designed to remove elements of visible light to enhance viewing. However, there is more to the electromagnetic spectrum than visible light. Many space telescopes employ filters to pick up emissions in X-rays, gamma rays and radio waves. Two very important filters that are used by the Hubble Space Telescope allow it to see in ultraviolet and infrared. These filters isolate the particular kind of light, and in so doing reveal workings of the Universe that are simply not visible to our eyes.

OBSERVING ACCESSORIES

SO YOU'VE
GOT A
TELESCOPE:
NOW WE'LL
SHOW YOU
WHICH
ACCESSORIES
ARE GOOD TO
GO WITH IT

Your telescope is the piece of kit that everyone admires. Your friends will look through it and the wonders of the Universe will be revealed to them. What they probably don't give a thought to, though, is the variety of accessories that enable the entire observing process to go as smoothly as it does.

When we talk about accessories we don't just mean nice toys, either. We're talking really useful bits of equipment that will help you get the best out of your telescope.

ESSENTIAL KIT

First on the list come finderscopes – these are invaluable for finding objects. Many smaller scopes come with a basic 5x24 finder, which means a 24mm lens with 5x magnification. But there are many upgrade options, and even moving up to a 6x30 version will improve things. Avoid a finderscope where the front lens is narrowed with an aperture stop. It also needs to have a crosshair for centring objects in its view.

Red-dot and reflex finders are the next step up from standard finders. Their magnification is zero – they show the sky as you see it with your eye. The most basic red-dot finders project a red dot onto a glass screen. When you look through the finder, the red dot appears among the stars. Just line the dot up by moving the telescope over the object you

Essential accessories
(from left): cleaning
kit, red light torch,
angled finderscope,
red-dot reflex finder
and dew shield

PAUL WHITFIELD X 4

ALSO ON THE LIST

POLAR SCOPE
This is also known as a polar alignment scope and it is used to help you align your telescope on the north celestial pole. This accurate alignment method is useful for anyone who's planning to photograph the night sky or observe with high magnification eyepieces.

MOTOR DRIVES
A motor drive is a very good accessory if you like to draw or photograph while you're observing. It means you won't need to twiddle dials constantly, as the drive does the job of keeping the scope pointing at the same place.

POWER PACK
Motor drives can run on batteries but these don't particularly like cold places, such as observing in the chill of the night, so they might not perform well. Another option is to buy a power pack – a rechargeable, longer-lasting power supply.

SCOPE COVER
After observing, if your scope is not being stored in its box, then the best way to keep it safe is to buy or make a complete scope cover. This will protect it from knocks, scratches and, more importantly, from dust and dirt.

wish to observe and there it will be in the main telescope's view. Other versions are available, such as the Telrad, which gives an unmagnified view with three red circles overlaid on it, like a bullseye.

Next up is a red torch – essential for being able to see in the black of night without ruining your dark-adapted eyes. You can buy them fairly cheaply, or you can adapt a torch you already own by covering the end in red acetate secured with a rubber band, or painting over the end with red nail varnish.

OTHER EXTRAS

Any astronomer will tell you that dew has a habit of gathering on the lens or mirror during a night session of stargazing. One way of keeping this night-time moisture off your equipment is to use a dew shield. These are available from all telescope retailers, but many people choose to make a shield for their scope as this is relatively simple to do. For example, you can get a thin, foam camping mat, cut it to size and wrap it around the tube.

Finally, but importantly, every astronomer should have a basic cleaning kit to keep their precious optics clean. This should contain a bottle of cleaning fluid, a micro-fibre cleaning cloth, a pack of cotton buds, some acid-free lens cleaning tissues, a soft retractable brush and a blower bulb for removing larger dirt particles.

KNOW YOUR SCOPE STATS

GET TO GRIPS WITH THE OFTEN MYSTERIOUS FIGURES THAT DESCRIBE THE OPTICAL PERFORMANCE OF YOUR TELESCOPE – FOCAL LENGTH AND FOCAL RATIO

1. FOCAL **LENGTH**

The focal length of a refracting telescope is the distance between its lens and the place where light rays from that lens are finally brought to a focus, known as the focal point. For a reflecting telescope, simply swap the word 'lens' for 'mirror'.

Focal length is one of the important numbers if you want to find out what magnification you are viewing the night sky with. The magnification is the focal length of your telescope divided by the focal length of your eyepiece. You get higher magnifications – good for viewing detail on the planets, for instance – with telescopes that have longer focal lengths. The downside to this is that longer focal

lengths mean smaller fields of view, which are not always best for observing wide star fields or star-hopping. You can, however, increase a telescope's focal length by using an accessory known as a Barlow lens.

Eyepieces also have focal lengths, but since they take the focused light and magnify the image into your eye, the numbers mean the reverse. So the smaller an eyepiece's focal length, the higher its magnification. For example, an 8mm focal length eyepiece gives you a 'closer' view than a 20mm eyepiece.

Focal point

3. VISUAL VS **PHOTO**

Bearing in mind what we've said about fast and slow scopes in the 'Focal ratio' section, the f/number will tell you whether a scope is particularly suited to observations with just the eye or whether it will be good for astrophotography too.

Smaller focal ratio (fast) telescopes are good for astrophotography – especially if you want to image large star fields – because they can get an image with shorter exposure

times than their long focal ratio counterparts. There's also less chance of stars blurring as a result of your mount's tracking falling behind the movement of the night sky.

If you're intending to mostly use your telescope for visual observing, then larger focal ratio (slow) instruments are ideal. To get 100x magnification with a small focal ratio (fast) telescope, you'd need to use a small focal length eyepiece. These often

have a fairly small exit pupil that can be uncomfortable to look through, especially if you have to wear glasses. Opting for a slower scope removes this problem. To get the same 100x magnification with a slower, large focal ratio scope you'd use a longer focal length eyepiece, which has longer and more comfortable eye relief.

Light path

2. FOCAL **RATIO**

The focal ratio of any telescope is its focal length divided by the diameter of the front lens or mirror. This leads to another way of describing it – the f/number. Let's say you end up with a '6' once you've done the calculation. The resulting focal ratio would be written as 'f/6'. A scope with an f/number lower than six is said to have a small focal ratio. F/numbers of nine or above are considered large. Knowing your focal ratio is important for astro imaging.

There's yet another way of describing a scope's focal ratio, as fast or slow, a throwback to the days when cameras used film. Small focal ratios meant the aperture of a camera's lens was open wide, which let in a lot of light and caused a 'fast' reaction between the chemicals on the film and the light. The opposite happened with large focal ratios: the narrower apertures in the lens let in less light, causing a 'slow' reaction with the light in the chemicals on the film.

F/NUMBER **PROS & CONS**

This general guide compares fast and slow focal ratios, and applies to most (but not all) telescopes

FAST	SLOW
Smaller focal ratio: f/4 and below	Larger focal ratio: f/9 and above
Shorter focal lengths: shorter telescope	Longer focal lengths: longer telescope
Wide field of view: good for observing large swathes of the night sky	Narrow field of view: good for zooming in on planets or viewing double stars
Smaller eyepiece eye relief: have to use lower magnifications or viewing can be uncomfortable	Larger eyepiece eye relief: can use higher magnifications
Smaller depth of focus: precise focusing required for a crisp image	Greater depth of focus: more tolerance in focusing
Telescopes can be smaller and easier to transport	Telescopes may be larger and heavier and so not as portable

BEST OF BOTH WORLDS

Choosing a telescope is not simply about deciding on the best focal ratio. It may be that portability overrides everything; many scopes languish in sheds and garages because they are too heavy or awkward to move. However, knowing the limitations of fast and slow telescopes is a useful addition to the buying process. If you want to hedge your bets, then it's best to go for the area between fast and slow scopes.

KNOW YOUR FIELD OF VIEW

DIFFERENT EQUIPMENT WILL SHOW YOU DIFFERENT PORTIONS OF THE SKY, BUT WHAT'S BEST FOR YOUR CHOSEN TARGET?

When you're out stargazing, the field of view is the amount of sky that you can see at any one time. It varies depending on what equipment you're using – here we show you how the appearance of the constellation of Cassiopeia changes when you look through different types of instrument.

THE NAKED EYE

Your eyes are excellent for expansive views of the constellations, asterisms, meteor showers, the Milky Way and big bright comets. Of course, you can see other objects, but it's the general majesty of the heavens that you get with such an amazing, near-180° left-to-right field of view. It makes the naked eye an enjoyable means of looking at the night sky. The main image here shows what the constellation of Cassiopeia looks like to the naked eye.

It's said that the eye has a magnification of 1x and the faintest stars you can see are mag. +6.0. Some people have claimed to be able to see stars as dim as mag. +7.0; even if you can, you'll still miss nearly all of the wondrous deep-sky objects and any hint of their structure. For these objects you need a pair of binoculars or a telescope.

9°

BINOCULARS

Using a standard pair of 10x50 binoculars you instantly increase your magnification to 10x, meaning things look 10 times bigger. Also, instead of the standard 5-7mm width of your pupils, you have the binocular's 50mm-diameter lenses to collect starlight. This allows you to see faint stars deep into mag. +10.0 territory.

The Double Cluster looks great through binoculars

Depending on the make, 10x50 binoculars have a field of view between 5° and 9°. This gives you lovely wide views to sweep across the sky in search of objects like nebulae, galaxies and star clusters, which look great through binoculars.

Just outside Cassiopeia there's something well worth viewing with binoculars, the Double Cluster in the constellation of Perseus. With the naked eye, you can just make it out as a faint smudge. Binoculars, though, reveal it as a true marvel: hundreds of stars in two distinct clusters spanning an area about 1° across. It's a stunning sight that easily fits into the field of view of a pair of 10x50 binoculars.

The 'W' shape of
the constellation of
Cassiopeia as it appears
to the naked eye

LARGE TELESCOPE

Bigger telescopes work with higher magnifications and narrow the fields of view further still, a result of their wider aperture. If you were to take a look at Cassiopeia using an 8-inch Dobsonian fitted with a 12mm Plössl lens, you would be looking with a magnification of over 100x that of your eye at an angular field of 0.5°.

Our target is the open cluster called Messier 52 (M52). Through binoculars, this object is simply a faint fuzzy patch. A small telescope begins to resolve the individual stars and shows its roundish appearance. However, a big Dobsonian reveals a fine group of about 200 stars with a diameter of about 0.25°, which fits easily into the field of view. M52 sits within the Milky Way, so the surrounding sky is full of stars and other treasures to investigate.

The large aperture of a Dobsonian scope means that you can see stars and other objects as faint as mag. +14.0. Dobsonians, though, are not built to track (follow) the sky. They point at the same fixed spot. This means that you'll see stars move across the sky as you look through the eyepiece. If your eyepiece increases the magnification to a powerful 400x, things will move across your field of view very fast indeed.

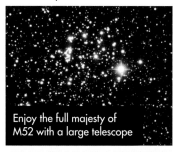

Enjoy the full majesty of
M52 with a large telescope

0.5°

1.3°

SMALL TELESCOPE

To see more detail than you get from binoculars you need a higher magnification and an instrument that captures more light. Welcome to the realm of the telescope.

Even with a small scope, like a 4-inch refractor fitted with a 26mm Plössl lens, you'll get a magnification of almost 40x greater than the eye. However, this comes at the cost of a reduced angular field of view, which goes down to about 1.3°. This kind of setup is useful for taking a look at double stars. Cassiopeia provides a

good example of this with mag. +7.4 Achird (Eta (η) Cassiopeiae), a red star with a brighter, mag. +3.0 yellow companion – though some people say the colours in this double are more golden and purple.

A small telescope will reveal objects well into the 12th magnitude and, because of its enhanced light-gathering power, things like the shapes of nebulae and detail on planets become apparent. Plus, for the first time in our equipment choices, you have the option to increase the magnification further by changing eyepieces.

You can split the beautiful double star Achird with a small scope

ASTROPHOTOGRAPHY

YOU DON'T NEED AN OBSERVATORY-SIZED TELESCOPE TO GET STARTED IN ASTRO IMAGING – YOU CAN TAKE STUNNING SPACE PHOTOS WITH A BASIC CAMERA AND A FEW OTHER BITS OF KIT

So you've seen some stunning images of star clusters and been inspired by marvellous vistas of the Milky Way, and now you're ready to try your hand at astrophotography yourself. As it happens you don't need any expert experience or equipment – you can take some fine astro images with a basic camera and a few other bits of kit. So, what do you need to get started?

There was a time when a 35mm film camera was the only way to go. These days, the best camera to have is the digital variety. Of course, the simplest point-and-shoot digital cameras are somewhat limited in their ability, and it's useful if you can turn off any automatic settings. But the wonder of any digital camera is that you can look at a photo straight after taking it. You can see if it's any good and make adjustments as necessary. With a 35mm film camera, you wouldn't have a clue what your pictures looked like until you got them back from being developed.

You might hear talk of CCD cameras or webcams in conversations about

Capture a steady view through a scope with an eyepiece bracket

astrophotography. For the absolute beginner, these bits of kit, which are attached to motor-driven telescopes, are a little too advanced. You can start using these when you become a more experienced astro imager.

GETTING GOOD RESULTS

Many books and articles confine astrophotography to when it's dark, but evening skies showing a crescent Moon, the planet Venus or noctilucent clouds make attractive subjects. When you're

Steady your camera with a tripod

GO FURTHER WITH A DSLR

Due to their vast array of functions and changeable lenses, the most versatile cameras for astro imaging are DSLRs. For sky shots, wide-angle lenses (20-35mm) are best because they capture a larger chunk of the sky, but the lens that comes with most of these cameras (normally 50mm) will also do a fine job. You can also adjust a DSLR lens to capture as much light from faint stars as possible by changing its aperture. This widens or narrows the diameter of the lens to let more or less light through. Apertures are measured using f/numbers; the wider the aperture, the smaller the f/number.

Improve your astro images by investing in a DSLR

shooting at twilight, check your camera's flash: if it's automatic it will want to do its thing. If you can, turn it off, or else you'll have to cover it up.

With the flash turned off, the camera's shutter will stay open for longer (in photography this is called a longer exposure) to gather the light it needs from the dim twilight – perhaps even for several seconds. If you're holding the camera by hand, it will be almost impossible not to wobble it a bit during the exposure, and this can introduce blur to your photos. To get around this you'll need a steady tripod. If you don't have a tripod, then resting a camera on a bean bag works just as well to keep the camera steady when taking a shot.

Another bit of kit called a cable release is also handy. This allows you to operate the shutter remotely and take a picture without causing any wobble as you press the capture button down. If your camera has

a time-delay feature, which is when it waits for 10 seconds or so before taking the shot, it's just as good as a cable release. Turn on the timer, press the button, stand back and wait for the shutter to open and close.

THE NEXT LEVEL

It really is amazing what you can achieve using just a camera on a tripod, let alone using it with a telescope. You can introduce your scope into the process very simply by holding the camera up to its eyepiece, positioning it where your eye would normally go. This way, you can get some great close-up images of the Moon. Again, wobbly hand syndrome is a real threat here. For greater stability there are brackets available that will hold your camera in place at the eyepiece, and they don't cost a fortune.

Now that we've whet your appetite, have a go at the three beginners' astrophotography projects we've set out over the page.

With a simple point-and-shoot camera you can capture a stunning night sky

TURN THE PAGE FOR 3 PHOTO PROJECTS

START SHOOTING
Learn how to capture the heavens

PROJECT 1
TWILIGHT SCENES

This is a great way to start your astrophotography journey. Look for a composition that includes a twilight sky, a low crescent Moon, and maybe even a planet or two. You'll get a better picture if you can frame the shot with some trees or buildings that will silhouette themselves against the sky.

If you have a DSLR, set it to manual so you can vary the results. Fix it to your tripod and open the camera's lens as wide as it will go (called a wide aperture). Focus at infinity and use different exposure times (vary how long the shutter stays open for). If you don't have a DSLR and your camera is of the point-and-click variety, try it anyway – the results could be surprising.

PROJECT 2
STAR TRAILS

The aim here is to capture the movement of the stars over time, showing you that Earth is spinning. As well as a tripod-mounted camera, you'll need a cable release. The camera has to gaze at the heavens for a long time to show the movement – exposures can be anything from 15 minutes to a few hours.

The longer you leave the camera shutter open the longer the star trails will be. On such long exposures, any light pollution will really show up, so the darker and clearer the skies the better. You'll get different effects depending on where your camera is pointing: aimed at the celestial pole the trails will appear circular; aimed at the celestial equator the trails will be straighter.

PROJECT 3
CLOSE-UP OF THE MOON

You get to use your telescope in this project. Focus it on the Moon, then hold the camera up to the eyepiece and click away. This type of astrophotography is known as afocal imaging. For the best results, use an eyepiece with a long eye-relief, because the camera lens may not be able to get as close to the eyepiece as your eye and you'll miss some of the image. That may happen anyway if your camera has a wider field of view than the eyepiece, so you may get some darkening around the image. You can minimise these effects and also reduce blurring from shaking hands by using a bracket clamp and the camera's optical zoom.

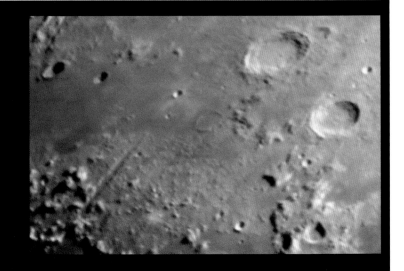

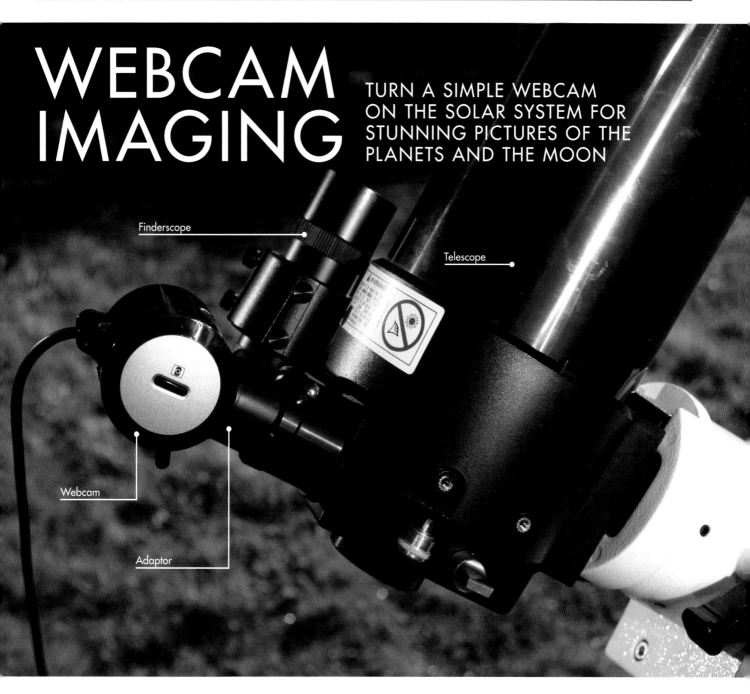

WEBCAM IMAGING

TURN A SIMPLE WEBCAM ON THE SOLAR SYSTEM FOR STUNNING PICTURES OF THE PLANETS AND THE MOON

Finderscope

Telescope

Webcam

Adaptor

WILL GATER

Digital photography has made taking pictures of celestial objects much easier. In days gone by, you needed all manner of telescope-mounting regalia for your camera, and then had to get the camera's film processed before you could see your pictures.

Then the CCD (charge-coupled device) camera arrived on the scene. A CCD is an electronic light sensor that's used in digital cameras. At first, only astro-imaging experts used them because CCDs came in big, heavy cameras with complicated controls and were expensive. But the era of digitally imaging the heavens had arrived.

Pretty soon the CCD and its electronic-light-sensor cousin the CMOS (complementary metal-oxide-semiconductor) chip found their way into a smaller, lighter, friendlier package called the

webcam. These were cheap and simple to use, so it's not surprising that they opened up digital astro imaging to everyone.

Webcams were originally developed to sit by your computer to make video calls and home movies, but soon astronomers found that they were also good at taking pictures of the night sky when fitted to a telescope. They're particularly well suited to the brighter objects in the Solar System like the Moon, Venus, Mars, Jupiter and Saturn.

A webcam works well on these subjects because it records a video comprised of many individual picture frames played quickly, one after the other. When you look at the Moon or the planets through a telescope, you also magnify imperfections in the atmosphere, which leads to shimmering and boiling

A Philips SPC900NC webcam sits in a telescope's eyepiece holder using an adaptor

MORE ADVICE OVER THE PAGE

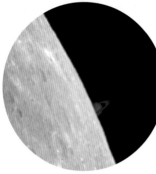

Captured with a webcam, from top to bottom: mountains on the Moon, Saturn pops out from behind the Moon, the crescent of Venus, Saturn and lunar craters

WILL GATER X 7, STEVE MARSH X 2

CREATE THE PERFECT SNAP

Your webcam movie file of a planet or the Moon will most likely be in a format called an AVI file. All it takes is a little computer wizardry to get a good-looking image or two from it.

For this, you'll need some software to process your movie file, and a good program to do this is called RegiStax. This great bit of software (free to download from www. astronomie.be/registax),

analyses the movie file from your webcam. It ignores each frame that is too badly affected by wind shake, your mount's tracking errors or too much turbulence in the atmosphere.

After dismissing the unsuitable shots, it's left with the best frames from the movie, which it then puts on top of one another to improve the detail, quality and colour in them – what's known as

stacking. These stacked frames may still be subtly different from one another, so the program will apply rotations, shifts, colour balances and other tweaks until it ends up with a brand-new, single, cleaned-up image. Stacking means the images you end up with are brighter and sharper. Indeed, it can sharpen your image so much that the final result is far better than the best original frame in the stack.

Sift the wheat from the chaff from an AVI file of Saturn with stacking software such as RegiStax

images. But there are fleeting moments when the atmosphere is calm, and since a webcam records many frames per second, it captures these calm moments when the view is perfect and the Moon and stars are at their best.

You can leave it at that, or you can then use several of these good frames from the movie to make your final image. You can do this, and more besides, with the help of a computer program to enhance your picture. See 'Create the perfect snap' above to find out how.

SHOOTING THE STARS

Webcams are designed to sit by a computer, so how do you attach one to a telescope? Well, first you have to remove the webcam's front lens and add an adaptor barrel in its place. You can buy special adaptor barrels from telescope suppliers, or you could use an old 35mm film canister, or even a bottle top with the end cut off – anything that's the right size to fit into the eyepiece slot.

The new adaptor barrel is then taped or glued to the webcam and the webcam is slotted into the telescope so that its light sensor chip is sitting where your eye would be to get a magnified view through your scope. You can see where the webcam sits in the photo on the previous page.

The Philips Toucam is often cited as a good webcam for astronomy but, sadly, Philips doesn't make it any longer. It's been replaced by newer models like the SPC230, which you can buy for

TOP WEBCAM TIPS

To get great images with your webcam, take a video that's around a minute long. Your stacking software can create a sharp final image from this. Also choose an observing site that doesn't have too many trees or houses. These give off heat, as can patios, creating swirling air currents that can cause your image to wobble. Setting up in the middle of a big field or by the sea is ideal.

Accurately focusing a webcam can be tricky. There are two ways to do this, depending on what you're imaging. For the Moon, frame the terminator in the webcam and use the contrasting features to gain focus. For planets, you can use a nearby bright star to focus the webcam before moving the scope's view back to the planet.

under £20. There are many other computer webcams available for a similar price too, such as the Logitech QuickCam and the Microsoft LifeCam. All of these webcams need their lenses adapting. If you don't fancy having a go yourself, some astronomy shops will offer a modification service.

Finally, regardless of what telescope and webcam you have, you'll need to connect it to a laptop computer to grab images of the night sky.

WHAT TO SEE

NIGHT-SKY OBJECTS THAT REVEAL THE COSMOS AT ITS MOST MAGNIFICENT

On a clear, dark night, there can be close to 2,000 stars in the sky, creating a celestial panorama of such inspiration that it is possible to understand why ancient civilisations created myths and legends for what they saw at night.

New let's be honest here, through a telescope most of the stars that make up this amazing wide-field view aren't that mesmerising. In many cases what you'll see is very similar to the naked-eye view – a point of light.

Don't be downhearted, however. In a Universe as vast as ours, there are enough wonders for a lifetime's worth of observing. The trick is to know where in the vast celstial spectacle to aim for.

So, in the pages that follow, you'll find the best objects to look at with all types of equipment, from the naked eye to binoculars and telescopes: double and variable stars, clusters and planets like magnificent Saturn; short-lived targets like meteors, comets and satellites. We cover distant objects within our Galaxy, and where to look to see next door – to the Andromeda Galaxy.

STEVE MARSH

YOUR FIRST FIVE SIGHTS

TOOLED UP AND READY TO GO, BUT DON'T KNOW WHERE TO AIM YOUR SCOPE? HERE'S OUR LIST OF THE TOP SIGHTS FOR BEGINNERS

Once you've got your first telescope, the Universe awaits

If you've just bought or been given your first telescope, you'll no doubt want to get out there and start using it. However, faced with the countless points of light in the night sky, it can be a daunting task to decide what to aim your telescope at first.

To make sure you're suitably impressed, we've highlighted five top sights that are easy to find if you're new to observing, yet that will be extremely impressive when you see them through a telescope for the first time. We've explained where and when to search for them (see right), and what to look for. This list will also give you a good taste of the sheer variety of different objects you can point your telescope at.

Heading up our list is the Moon – the best place for any fledgling astronomer to start is our nearest celestial neighbour. You haven't really seen this familiar celestial body until you've viewed it with a telescope; its rugged, crater-marked surface will keep you coming back to your new scope for more.

Next, you'll want to bag yourself a planet, and Jupiter – the largest of them all – makes a stunning sight. We then take you to deep space and the famous Orion Nebula, a huge cloud of gas and dust hanging in Orion's Sword. Indeed, a relatively cheap telescope with an aperture of 3- to 6-inches will show you a wide variety of astronomical objects, and our final two targets are a distant galaxy and a pair of star clusters.

You could just rush outside and get going. But, with a little preparation, your session can be even more enjoyable. Use a star chart to get your bearings as to where the different constellations are, to help you find each of the five objects. Once you're at the scope, with your eyes properly adjusted to the dark after 20 minutes or so outside, you're ready to go.

What you won't see are grand, colourful objects that look like the stunning Hubble telescope images you see in books and on TV. However, what you will get is a feeling of great satisfaction as you find these incredible objects for yourself!

TELESCOPE TARGETS
FOR BEGINNERS

Five impressive, easy-to-spot objects to get you started

❮ THE MOON

Constellation: It doesn't stay in the same place but it's hard to miss

When to view: During waxing phases – not at full Moon

The best times to view the Moon are during its waxing phases, from the date when it is first seen as a thin crescent emerging after sunset. The reason you want to look at this time is that this is when the terminator is visible. This is the line between the lighted side and the dark side of the Moon, and is the place where the Sun's light catches the craters and mountain ranges, thus casting amazing shadows across the lunar surface.

⌃ JUPITER

Constellation: Various

When to view: From September 2012 until April 2013

Through a small telescope you can see the planet as a disc, with several dark bands in its atmosphere. You may also see Jupiter's four largest moons as points of light either side of it. As it's a planet, there are times of year when Jupiter is not visible.

❮ ORION NEBULA, M42

Constellation: Orion

When to view: Orion is only visible during the winter months

The Orion Nebula, numbered 42 in the famous Messier Catalogue, is a 'must' for winter observers. The nebula is just visible to the unaided eye as a misty patch, but even the smallest of scopes will start to reveal the sweeping structure of this stellar nursery.

❮ ANDROMEDA GALAXY, M31

Constellation: Andromeda

When to view: Late summer and early autumn

M31 is found by star-hopping from the nearby Great Square of Pegasus. It will appear as a misty patch but is actually a giant, spiral island of stars, similar to our own Milky Way. What you are looking at sits at around 2.75 million lightyears away.

⌃ SWORD HANDLE DOUBLE CLUSTER, NGC 869 & NGC 884

Constellation: Perseus

When to view: Winter months

The Sword Handle will be high in the east, moving almost overhead through the night. To find it, locate the 'W' of Cassiopeia and work from there. With a small telescope it's a wondrous sight of two amazing, roundish concentrations of hundreds of stars.

STEVE MARSH X 2, WILL GATER X 3, JON HICKS, PAUL WHITFIELD

STAR CLUSTERS IN BINOCULARS

THROUGH A PAIR OF BINOCULARS, STAR CLUSTERS ARE VIBRANT, DEEP-SPACE JEWELS. HERE ARE SOME TIPS ON HOW AND WHEN TO OBSERVE THEM

When you gaze up at the night sky, it looks like a lot of stars are on their own. But a solitary-looking star may be a member of a vast group that's travelling through space as a unit. If we wind the clock back millions of years, we may find the stars of one of these families forming in the same vast cloud of dust and gas, known as a nebula.

Known as open clusters, these families of anywhere from a few dozen to a few thousand stars are created in the dusty spiral arms of our Galaxy. They travel together through space, but gentle tidal forces eventually cause the stars to move apart until they begin to merge into the general starry background.

There are many fine examples of newer and older clusters out there that are perfect for looking at with binoculars. As a rule of thumb, you can pretty much assume that the younger the open cluster, the more compact it appears, since the stars haven't had much time to drift apart.

TITANIC GLOBULARS

There is another variety of star cluster out there: the globular cluster. These are much bigger than the open sort, consisting of hundreds of thousands or millions of generally reddish, older stars. Whereas open clusters are found and made within the plane of our Galaxy, globular clusters form a halo around it and their creation is much less well understood.

In terms of observing, this all means that the majority of open clusters are found in or close to that misty river of stars stretching across the sky, the Milky Way, while globular clusters are seen all over the sky. When looking at them with the naked eye you'll see only fuzzy patches, but a pair of binoculars will reveal some truly spectacular gems.

A pair of 10x50 binoculars is the perfect way to enjoy the full majesty of star clusters

TEN STAR CLUSTERS
YOU MUST SEE

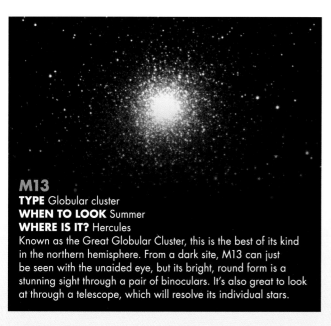

M13
TYPE Globular cluster
WHEN TO LOOK Summer
WHERE IS IT? Hercules
Known as the Great Globular Cluster, this is the best of its kind in the northern hemisphere. From a dark site, M13 can just be seen with the unaided eye, but its bright, round form is a stunning sight through a pair of binoculars. It's also great to look at through a telescope, which will resolve its individual stars.

M45
TYPE Open cluster
WHEN TO LOOK Winter
WHERE IS IT? Taurus
The Pleiades, or Seven Sisters, is one of the most splendid clusters in the night sky. With the naked eye, six stars of the cluster are easy to see, but counting up to 10 is possible. The cluster actually contains many hundreds of stars, and a decent pair of binoculars will be able to reveal many of them.

M7
TYPE Open cluster
WHEN TO LOOK Summer
WHERE IS IT? Scorpius
Also known as Ptolemy's Cluster, this appears to be twice the size of the full Moon. To the eye, the 80 stars of the cluster appear as a bright clump in the Milky Way, but through binoculars the stars are resolved against the more distant milky band of the Galaxy, making this a fine sight indeed.

M5
TYPE Globular cluster
WHEN TO LOOK Summer
WHERE IS IT? Serpens
This is thought to be one of the oldest of all globular clusters. It is easily found in binoculars and has a slightly oval-shaped appearance. What you'll see is a fuzzy blob, hinting at the vast number of stars it contains. Through a telescope, curving groups of stars appear to spiral out from the centre.

M35
TYPE Open cluster
WHEN TO LOOK
Autumn and winter
WHERE IS IT? Gemini
This cluster contains upwards of 200 stars and can just be seen with the unaided eye on good clear nights. Binoculars bring out the brightest 20 or so stars, while the rest form a diffuse oval wash behind. It sits in a lovely star-spattered area of the Milky Way.

M22
TYPE Globular cluster
WHEN TO LOOK Summer
WHERE IS IT? Sagittarius
M22 is easily visible with the unaided eye, and a great object through binoculars. It's larger than M13, which makes it impressive in itself, but sitting in the river of stars that is the Milky Way makes this a real jewel in the crown.

M44
TYPE Open cluster
WHEN TO LOOK Spring
WHERE IS IT? Cancer
Known as the Beehive Cluster, M44 contains hundreds of stars and can be seen as a misty patch with the naked eye. Due to its large size, binoculars are the best way to see M44: through them you'll see a dozen or so of its brightest stars.

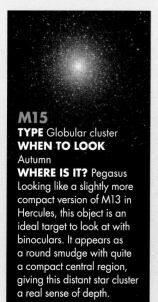

M15
TYPE Globular cluster
WHEN TO LOOK
Autumn
WHERE IS IT? Pegasus
Looking like a slightly more compact version of M13 in Hercules, this object is an ideal target to look at with binoculars. It appears as a round smudge with quite a compact central region, giving this distant star cluster a real sense of depth.

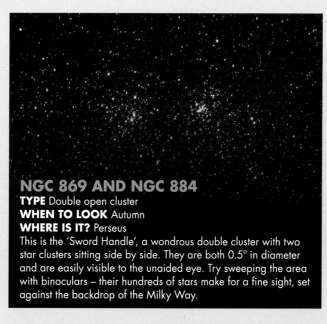

NGC 869 AND NGC 884
TYPE Double open cluster
WHEN TO LOOK Autumn
WHERE IS IT? Perseus
This is the 'Sword Handle', a wondrous double cluster with two star clusters sitting side by side. They are both 0.5° in diameter and are easily visible to the unaided eye. Try sweeping the area with binoculars – their hundreds of stars make for a fine sight, set against the backdrop of the Milky Way.

M3
TYPE Globular cluster
WHEN TO LOOK
Spring and summer
WHERE IS IT? Canes Venatici
This is another stunning globular cluster. It can just be seen with the unaided eye, but binoculars will reveal its bright, round shape that holds around 500,000 stars.

DOUBLE STARS

THE SIGHT OF TWO STARS PARTNERED TOGETHER CAN BE TRULY STUNNING, ESPECIALLY WHEN THEY HAVE VIBRANT COLOURS. BUT DON'T CONFUSE YOUR BINARIES WITH YOUR OPTICAL DOUBLES...

After the invention of the telescope in the early 17th century, the true nature of the night sky became apparent for the first time. What had been mere fuzzy blobs as seen by the unaided eye now had form, and suddenly a whole new world of nebulae, galaxies and star clusters could be observed.

When those first telescopes were trained on the stars, an interesting discovery was made: that not all the stars we see as single points of light with our eyes are, in fact, alone. Some were revealed to be two stars or maybe even more. Double stars and multiple star systems were discovered. As the number of double stars being found grew, it became necessary to divide the category up further, in order to clarify exactly what sort of double star it was.

To understand the first category, optical doubles, imagine the true 3D nature of space with stars sprinkled all over the place. From our viewpoint, one star may appear very close to another star, but this is only because the two stars happen to lie in the same direction from us in space; in fact, these stars are not linked in any way. One of them could be much further away from us than the other, but stargazing-wise, we have no way of knowing, because everything in the night sky looks the same distance away from us.

Then there are the double stars that are linked by gravity. If you see one of these you're looking at a binary star. It's no coincidence that the stars of a double appear to be in the same place: they are both the same distance from us, and they orbit around each other. It's estimated by some scientists that perhaps half of the stars in our Galaxy may be binaries, although binaries account for only five per cent of stars observed so far.

So how do you know which is which? Well, unless your magazine or star atlas tells you, simply by gazing at the sky there is no way of telling whether you're looking at an optical double or a binary. Only with the careful study of the movements in a double star can we gauge whether the stars are gravitationally bound to each other or not.

INTERACTING STARS

If you're looking up at a binary star system, it's fascinating to know what could be happening with the stars themselves. This is because sometimes the stars in a binary system can interact – especially when one of the stars is more massive than the other. In this case, gas can be pulled off the smaller companion, which can lead

TOP 5 DOUBLES TO OBSERVE

1. ALBIREO
Constellation: Cygnus
Albireo is a lovely golden and blue double that's a binary star system. The golden component is mag. +3.1, while the blue member is mag. +5.1. You'll need a scope to see the pair.

2. ALMACH
Constellation: Andromeda
The third brightest star in Andromeda is Almach. It's made up of a brighter yellow star of mag. +2.3, close to a mag. +5.1 greenish companion. To resolve them you'll need to use a telescope.

3. THE DOUBLE DOUBLE
Constellation: Lyra
To the naked eye, Epsilon Lyrae's two yellow stars have a similar brightness of mag. +5.5. However, with a scope you'll see that each part in fact has its own binary companion.

4. MIZAR AND ALCOR
Constellation: Ursa Major
Zeta and 80 Ursae Majoris are an optical double. The ability to see the two white stars, mags. +2.2 and +4.0, with the naked eye was a traditional test of how good your eyesight was.

to tremendously destructive stellar explosions called novae.

Of course, you won't see any of this going on when you look through a telescope, but double stars are still amazing targets to aim at. Some doubles show startling colour differences between the two stars – you may see, for example, a shimmering yellow star next to a vivid blue one – while with other double stars, the two will be more or less the same brightness, yet sit startlingly close together. If you can spot our top five favourite doubles, which we've listed below, we have no doubt that you'll soon be hooked on these jewels of the night sky.

Albireo is a beautiful binary star with striking gold and blue components

5. PHAEO AND PHAESYLA
Constellation: Taurus
This orange and white optical double is easily visible to the naked eye, with mags +3.8 and +3.4 respectively. Also called Theta Tauri, it is part of the Hyades star cluster.

TESTING YOUR SCOPE

You can use double stars to test your telescope's optics. How well you can split the stars depends on the quality of your optics, as well as the size of your telescope's aperture, or front lens.

If you have a good-quality small telescope, say four inches in diameter, you should be able to see doubles up to 1.15 arcseconds apart, if seeing conditions are perfect. Our top five doubles on the left should all be easily within your reach.

To split double stars closer than this, you need a larger telescope. To find out the closest double stars a telescope will theoretically split, you just divide 4.6 by the diameter of the telescope's front lens in inches. It's a theoretical figure, though, because if the atmosphere is fairly turbulent then you won't be able to see the components of a really close double star as well.

OBSERVING VARIABLE STARS

NOT ALL STARS APPEAR TO SHINE AS BRIGHTLY ALL OF THE TIME – SOME APPEAR TO WAX AND WANE

Algol, the middle star in the row of three just below centre, is an eclipsing binary with a period of nearly three days

At first glance, or even after a prolonged stare, it can seem like the starlit night changes very little. Apart from the slow movement of the sky caused by Earth's rotation and the odd meteor, nothing much else appears to happen.

However, if you know when and where to look, even the seemingly fixed stars can take on a life of their own. After a little investigation, you'll see that the night sky is, in fact, constantly changing. This is because of variable stars, stellar wonders that change in brightness over time. Some do so in just a few hours, while others take several years.

Variables come in many forms, the main types being intrinsic and extrinsic variables. If you're looking for action, then look out for an intrinsic variable. The changes in these objects happen within the star itself. It may pulsate in and out, for example, getting brighter and fainter as it goes.

One type of intrinsic is the long-period variable. These tend to be unstable older stars fighting internal battles with gravity and pressure, resulting in them growing and shrinking over long periods of time. They make good observing targets: some can be seen with the naked eye when they are at their brightest, yet they can then dim to a point where only a pair of binoculars or a telescope will reveal them.

The action really starts to hot up with another group of intrinsic stars called cataclysmic – or explosive – variables, which pull gas off their close neighbours. The pile-up of new gas leads to nuclear explosions, called novae, which in turn result in a dramatic, sudden increase in brightness. The dying explosions of old stars, called supernovae, are also part of this group.

Add in the eruptive variables, which include stars whose surfaces flare up from time to time, and it's clear how active the intrinsic type really is.

OUTSIDE INFLUENCE

Meanwhile, extrinsic variables owe their changeable nature to an external element in the mix. Take an eclipsing binary, for example – this is where the orbits of two close stars are such that, from our perspective on Earth, one appears to move in front of the other as they go around. The amount of light we see coming from the system as a whole changes whenever one of the stars moves in front of the other.

Another extrinsic variety is the rotating variable. These stars spin so fast that their light output is actually affected: if we could see them they would have a squashed appearance. Professional astronomers have discovered extrinsic variables at incredible distances in the Large Magellanic Cloud. The variability of these stars is controlled by a light-bending phenomenon called gravitational microlensing.

That may be a little far away for our equipment, but watching out for the fluctuating light of variable stars is a perfect project for amateur astronomers. With a relatively inexpensive telescope, you can add useful observations to the knowledge bank that professional astronomers may use to study how the Universe works. There are so many variable stars out there that they would never be able to look at them all without your help.

STARRY MEASURING STICKS

Cepheids are intrinsic variable stars that are useful to astronomers because they have a very regular period of light change. Some change just once day, while others take a month or more to complete their cycle. The period is linked precisely with the true brightness of the star – so a Cepheid with a five-day period near to us is the same true brightness as a five-day Cepheid in a distant galaxy. As we know exactly how light diminishes with distance, we can work out how much farther away the distant Cepheid is, using it to help measure distances in space.

FIVE FAMOUS VARIABLES

DELTA CEPHEI
Type: Pulsating variable; it's also the prototype of all Cepheid variables
Range: Mag. +3.9 down to mag. +5.0
Period: 5 days 9 hours
Best time to see: Autumn
Constellation: Cepheus
Equipment: Naked eye

MIRA
Type: Long-period red giant; the first of its type, its variability was discovered in 1596
Range: Mag. +2.0 down to mag. +10.1
Period: 332 days
Best time to see: Autumn
Constellation: Cetus
Equipment: Binoculars

RASALGETHI
Type: Massive semi-regular old red supergiant
Range: Mag. +2.8 down to mag. +4.0
Period: About 3 months
Best time to see: Summer
Constellation: Hercules
Equipment: Naked eye

ALGOL
Type: Eclipsing binary
Range: Mag. +1.6 down to mag. +3.0
Period: 2 days 21 hours; brightens over 10 hours
Best time to see: Autumn
Constellation: Perseus
Equipment: Naked eye

RS OPHIUCHI
Type: Recurrent nova
Range: Mag. +5.0 down to mag. +12.5
Period: Around 20 years
Best time to see: Summer
Constellation: Ophiuchus
Equipment: Telescope; naked eye when bright

INTRODUCING THE MOON

THE MOON WAS MADE WAY BACK WHEN A LARGE CHUNK OF CHEDDAR THE SIZE OF MARS HIT EARTH. TRUE? NO! HOLD ON TO YOUR DOUBLE GLOUCESTER AS THIS MYTH, AND OTHERS, ARE ABOUT TO BE DISPROVED

To state a fact: the Moon is always around somewhere in the sky at some time or other. It sounds obvious, but this concept is wrapped up in urban myth and provoked a great discussion among planetarium presenters recently. The myth in question has two parts, both of which are entirely wrong: firstly, the Moon comes out at night; and secondly, it's invisible during the day. No names will be mentioned here to protect the guilty, but I was told by a science teacher just the other day (which makes the following even worse to absorb), that the myth is taught in a particular primary school because the pupils would be uncomfortable with the truth. I'd suggest that maybe the wrong teacher is in charge of science.

MYTH-BUSTING

Understanding the Moon's orbit around Earth and the corresponding way it is lit by the Sun, which leads to its phases (see box, lower right), is not easy. However, with a bit of patience it is possible to appreciate why the Moon can be visible during the day and does not only 'come out' when it's dark at night.

The question really should be: why don't we notice the Moon during the day? The simple answer is that the sky is brighter during the day than at night, so the Moon is not as prominent. There are lots of other reasons why, such as the fact that evenings are the part of the day when we generally have more time to gaze at the sky, whereas we're all busy rushing around during the day.

So, yesterday, after one such busy day at work I took the time as night approached to do some stargazing and watched the full Moon rise over the trees in the field in front of our house. To the naked eye, this is when the Moon is most magnificent: a low, golden-tinged globe slowly being carried into the sky by the rotating Earth. It's when the Moon is low that it's possible to notice this movement the most and, if you have time, it's worth noting where it is an hour later – you may be surprised how far it has moved.

A couple of other things that are deserving of special attention are the Moon's colour and its movement across the sky as it orbits Earth.

The Moon moves at a blistering Mach 3, which is three times the speed of sound at sea level. The stronger goldish-to-reddish colour of the rising Moon, as opposed to the grey-white view when it's higher, is explained by the fact that when it's low to the horizon, light from the Moon

SEAS AND HIGHLANDS

An unaided, naked-eye view of the full Moon reveals dark patches, some roundish in appearance, that sit within a much brighter landscape. Early astronomers thought these dark areas were great volumes of water. Even though we know that water doesn't exist on the Moon, their old watery names have remained in use to this day. So, on 20 July 1969 man first landed on the Moon in Mare Tranquilitatis – the Sea of Tranquility. My favourite wet feature name on the Moon is Palus Putredinis – the Marsh of Decay; a splendid name!

The dark patches on the lunar surface were thought to be watery features like seas and marshes by early astronomers

PHASES

The word Moon is responsible for our word 'month': one mooneth (or thereabouts) was the measurement of the time it took for the Moon to complete one orbit of the Earth in relation to the Sun. Although it's given in schools as 28 days, the Moon's changing appearance (it's cycle of phases) takes just over 29.5 days. This is known as the Synodic Month. It represents the period from one full Moon to the next (or any other

BY DAY

Contrary to popular myth, the Moon does come out during the day

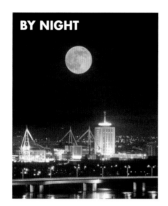

BY NIGHT

The full Moon reflects the Sun's light and has no illumination of its own

EARTHSHINE

The Sun is the main object that lights the Moon, but Earth also has an effect. Our planet is over 3.5 times the diameter of the Moon, so we reflect more light onto its surface than the Moon gives us when it is full. This is called earthshine and it can be seen as a faint glow on the unlit part of the Moon when it is a thin crescent (before and after a new Moon).

gets filtered through Earth's atmosphere. All the particles that make this up scatter the blue light, which leaves mostly red light to reach us when we're watching the spectacle on the ground.

A MOVING MOON

As for the Moon's own travels, try and find a star very close to its left side. An hour later the Moon will have passed over the star, which should now be sitting to the Moon's right. The Moon may not completely cover the star, sometimes the star will just graze its top or bottom. You'll have more success seeing this if

the Moon is not full, as its light washes out most nearby stars.

The passing of the Moon in front of the star or planet, blocking it, is known as an occultation and these are listed in the handbook of the British Astronomical Association. If you've never seen a star being blinked out by the Moon, then you have an assignment – go out and see one! Even better is a planet: Venus or Saturn are my favourites. Saturn is especially good: with a scope you can watch as the rings are slowly covered by the Moon, dipping in and out of the lunar valleys before finally disappearing.

OF THE MOON

identical phase, for example half Moon to half Moon). The Sun is always shining on one half of the Moon – how much of the lighted side we see depends on where the Moon is in orbit around Earth. The new Moon happens when the Moon sits between us and the Sun, and so the far side is lit (this is also the only time a solar eclipse can occur).

As the Moon moves around Earth and each day passes, we see more and more of its lighted side, a waxing (growing) evening crescent first, then half Moon, waxing gibbous and finally full Moon. At this point, the Moon sits on completely the opposite side of the sky to the Sun. Now everything reverses and the waning (shrinking) phases go through gibbous, half and waning morning crescent, finally back to new.

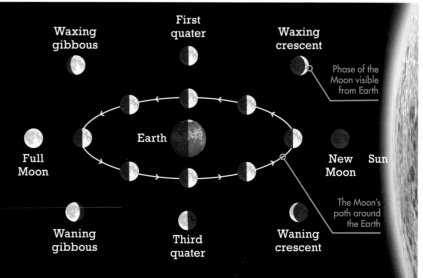

Waxing gibbous

First quater

Waxing crescent

Phase of the Moon visible from Earth

Earth

Full Moon

New Moon

Sun

The Moon's path around the Earth

Waning gibbous

Third quater

Waning crescent

OBSERVING THE MOON

THE MOON: IT'S BIG, ROUND AND BRIGHT. ANYONE CAN DISCOVER ITS FINER DETAILS, WHETHER IT'S WITH THE NAKED EYE OR BINOCULARS

Some astronomers seem to get a complex about the Moon. It's not that they're affected by it in werewolfish ways, but rather they develop a loathing for our large, rocky satellite. Why? Well, these usually friendly astronomers come to see it as a natural light polluter, washing away all the faint, small and fuzzy galaxies and nebulae they like to view. To them, the Moon is more of a nuisance than an object that's worthy of observing.

This is a real shame as the Moon has so much to offer. There's simply no truth in the assertion that when 'you've seen it once, you've seen it all' – with binoculars and small telescopes the appearance of the Moon can change dramatically from one hour to the next. Another reason it's so good is that it's easy to find. There's no star-hopping or fiddling with finderscopes, as the Moon quite plainly hangs about just waiting for you to look at it.

MAGNIFY THE VIEW

The Moon is a stunning object to look at, but there are times when binoculars or a telescope are the only things that'll do it justice: for example, the first few days after new Moon through to just before full Moon. During this period, when the Moon is waxing, we see a sunlit, happy side and a contrasting unlit, spooky side.

The views of the bright side give us the names of the phases: crescent, half, gibbous and full. After full Moon the phases reverse as it starts waning; these are equally worth a look. However, the post-full phases are generally seen very late in the night, when most people prefer to sleep.

The zone between the light and dark sections of the Moon is known as the 'terminator', and this is the place to concentrate on for the most stunning lunar views. It's along the waxing Moon's terminator that, if you were standing on the lunar surface, the Sun would be rising.

The low light hits its mountains, craters, valleys, crinkly ridges, rilles, escarpments and all manner of other volcanic and impact features, casting dramatic shadows across the stark landscape. The view is further enhanced by largely flat, dark areas of solidified lava known as the lunar seas, over which shadows can stretch for tens of kilometres. All of this

EXPERIENCING ECLIPSES

Why do eclipses occur so infrequently? It all has to do with the Moon's tilted orbit

Over the course of a year the Sun moves across the sky on a path known as the ecliptic. It rises in the east and sets in the west, in essence appearing like it travels around Earth.

If the Moon orbited Earth in this same plane, then each month we would get an eclipse of the Sun (when the Moon passes between the Sun and Earth) and an eclipse of the Moon (when the Earth is between the Sun and the Moon). We don't, however, as the Moon's orbit is tilted at an average of 5° from the ecliptic.

Most months this means that from our point of view on Earth, the Moon moves above or below the Sun at new Moon, and above or below Earth's shadow at full Moon. We only get an eclipse when the Moon's orbit intersects the ecliptic and all three bodies are in the correct alignment.

During a total solar eclipse the Sun's outer atmosphere is visible

Due to a fantastic coincidence, the Sun is 400 times bigger than the Moon, but around 400 times further away. This means that they appear to be the same size. The Moon just covers the Sun during a total solar eclipse, allowing us to witness its ghostly outer atmosphere, known as the corona.

LUNAR ATLASES

There are many atlases and wall charts vying to help you find the various craters, mountains and features of the Moon. They have their strengths and weaknesses, and you'll find some easier to use than others.

Watch out for any that flip the Moon so that south becomes north, or make any other change to orientation. These are fine for seasoned astronomers who use a specific telescope setup to observe the Moon, but for those of us who switch between correcting lenses, terrestrial telescopes, binoculars and the like, go for a plain and simple map with north at the top. It's also an advantage to have one with high-quality pictures.

Wall charts are also good for getting a general idea of where things are on the Moon. However, they're less use at the eyepiece unless they're safely wrapped up in a dew-proof coating, so it's worth getting a laminated version.

A lunar map will help you get to know the Moon's features

gradually changes as the Moon spins on its axis, but even at this slow rate you will be able to see hour-by-hour movement.

That the Moon spins on its axis may seem strange, as we know the same side always faces Earth. We are actually able to see 59 per cent of its surface as the Moon 'wobbles' up and down and from left to right, an effect known as libration.

We only see the one face because a long time ago the molten material inside the Moon caused it to become tidally locked to Earth. This 'synchronous rotation' means that the Moon spins once on its axis in exactly the same time it takes to orbit Earth. You can get an idea of how this works if you imagine yourself observing from the Sun. Over the course of a month you would see the Moon spin once.

Of course, leaving Earth takes a bit of mastering, but once you can imagine it, understanding the Universe becomes a breeze.

LATIN LINGO

When you look at a map of the Moon, you'll notice that its physical features all have Latin names because they were named a long time ago when Latin was more widely used. Here's what those names mean in modern English.

Catena .. Chain of craters
Dorsum .... Mare ridge
Dorsa .. Group of mare ridges
Lacus .... Lake
Mare .... Seas
Mons .... Mountain
Montes .. Mountain range
Oceanus .... Ocean
Palus .... Marsh
Promontorium ..... Cape
Rima .... Fissure
Rimae ... Group of fissures
Rupes .... Escarpment
Sinus .... Bay
Terra .... Landmass
Terrae .... Highlands
Vallis .... Valleys

TOP TEN MOON SIGHTS

OUR CELESTIAL NEIGHBOUR HAS ENOUGH TO KEEP ASTRONOMERS BUSY FOR A LIFETIME, BUT HERE ARE 10 HIGHLIGHTS FOR TELESCOPES AND BINOCULARS

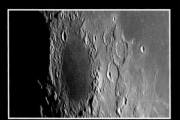

CRATER GRIMALDI
SIZE: 173km across
TYPE: Basin
APPEARANCE: Visible even to the naked eye, this dark basin reveals fantastic detail through binoculars and telescopes, such as eroded walls, ridges and low hills.

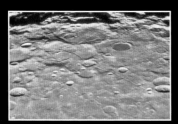

RIMAE SIRSALIS
SIZE: 425km long
TYPE: Rille system
APPEARANCE: This series of fault lines is visible even in a small telescope, which will reveal Sirsalis's main crack running straight for over 300km through a cratered environment.

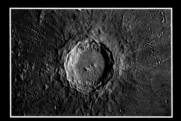

CRATER COPERNICUS
SIZE: 94km across
TYPE: Impact crater
APPEARANCE: One of the Moon's recognisable features and the result of quite a recent impact, a scope reveals terraced crater walls and central peaks rising from the floor below.

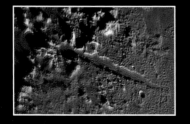

VALLIS ALPES
SIZE: 155km long
AGE: Valley and rille
APPEARANCE: A clean gouge through a mountainous region, the 18km-wide fault line can be easily visible in small scope and binoculars as a dark stripe in a lighter landscape.

CRATER PLATO

SIZE: 109km across
TYPE: Lava-filled impact crater
APPEARANCE: In binoculars and small telescopes the beauty of this crater is its jagged rim with 2km high mountains compared to its smooth lava-filled floor.

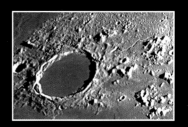

MONTES ALPES

SIZE: 3.4km maximum height
TYPE: Mountain range
APPEARANCE: Through binoculars you will just be able to make out this rangle of peaks; with a telescope they start to reveal really good detail, especially if the terminator is close by.

MONTES TENERIFFE

SIZE: 2.5km maximum height
TYPE: Mountain range
APPEARANCE: When caught in the right angle of sunlight this 110km-long mountain range reveals good detail among its peaks using a small scope and around 150x magnification.

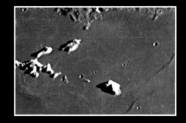

MONS PITON

SIZE: 2.2km in height
TYPE: Mountain
APPEARANCE: Lying on its own in the flat region of the Mare Imbrium, use a small telescope when the Sun's illumination is low to reveal the shadow cast by this lone peak.

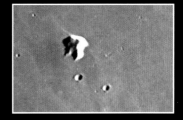

RUPES RECTA

SIZE: 110km long
TYPE: Rille
APPEARANCE: This popular target for binoculars and small telescopes is another fault line where the lunar surface suddenly drops by 300m. It's best seen when close to the terminator.

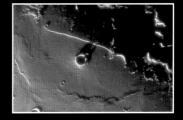

VALLIS RHEITA

SIZE: 450km long
TYPE: Valley
APPEARANCE: A long, wide valley that many think is the result of a sustained meteor bombardment. A small telescope will show the crater Rheita next door has a central peak.

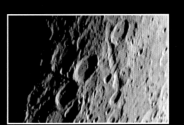

OBSERVING THE SUN

WHEN THE SHORT SUMMER NIGHTS AND LONG SUNNY DAYS COME AROUND, THERE'S NO NEED TO FRET ABOUT WHAT TO SEE – THE DAYTIME HAS ITS OWN HIGHLIGHT

Stars are fascinating things: at the simplest level they make the patterns of the constellations. Some brighter examples give hints of colour, like red Betelgeuse in Orion. The trouble is, every night-time example is so incredibly far away. Fortunately, the Sun is one star that's right on our doorstep and it's available for everyone to look at, understand and, depending on how you're looking at it, gasp in amazement.

The Sun, our source of natural light and warmth, and the star that made life possible on our planet, is just next door in astronomical terms. On average, it's only 150 million kilometres away.

However, the Sun's close proximity makes it brighter and hotter than any other star in the sky. Never look at the Sun using just your eyes, unfiltered binoculars or telescopes – you risk permanent damage to your eyesight. There are a number of options to view the Sun safely.

If you have a refracting telescope, try the projection method. Line the telescope up with the Sun (remembering not to look at the Sun through the telescope) and then hold up a piece of card close to the eyepiece so that an image of the Sun falls onto it.

When projecting the Sun, you'll be able to see that its disc appears slightly darker around the edges than it is in the middle, an effect known as limb-darkening. You'll also be able to see sunspots – providing there are any around. Project the Sun over a few days and you might see the sunspots move and change shape because the Sun rotates quite slowly.

FILTERING OPTIONS

If you want to move on from projecting, you can buy filters that fit over the big, front lens of your telescope. These objective lens filters allow you to look directly through the telescope at the Sun. Because it's quite risky to point your scope at the Sun, these filters must fit properly and must not be damaged in any way. Before you go out to observe the Sun, be sure to seek expert advice from a reputable astronomy shop.

Solar filters block out what you don't want to reach your eye: the Sun's infrared heat, its ultraviolet radiation and 99.9 per cent of its light. What you get is a greatly dimmed, safe image of the Sun. You'll be able to see sunspots and those dark solar edges through the scope and, depending on what kind of filter you buy, the Sun will be displayed in a different colour. The cheaper 'white-light' filters are made of mylar (aluminium plastic sheet), which gives the Sun a blue tinge, while more expensive glass white-light filters give a more natural orange-yellow look to the Sun's disc (see 'Sights on the Sun', on page 84).

Then there are the costly hydrogen-alpha (H-alpha) and calcium-K (CaK) filters and dedicated telescopes. These filter all the light and heat coming from the Sun except in wavelengths of hydrogen-alpha or calcium.

At the H-alpha wavelengths, you'll get orange views of the features in part of the Sun's atmosphere called the chromosphere, where dramatic solar flares and outbursts called prominences take place.

Looking through a CaK filter allows you to see magnetic storms that occur lower in the chromosphere, all in a fetching purple. So although these are two expensive options, they certainly produce the 'wow' factor when looking at the Sun.

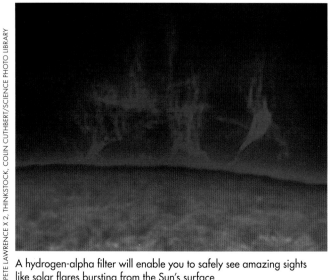

A hydrogen-alpha filter will enable you to safely see amazing sights like solar flares bursting from the Sun's surface

MORE
ADVICE
OVER THE
PAGE

You can observe the Sun safely
by spending just a few pounds
on a pair of solar eclipse glasses

THE **CORONA**

The amazing sight of the Sun's outer atmosphere, the corona, only becomes visible to us on Earth at totality – the height of a total solar eclipse. Of course, the corona is always there, it is simply that its delicate pearly-white structure is usually drowned out by the brightness of the Sun and our daytime sky. Views of the corona can also change quite dramatically depending on how active the Sun is; its shape is influenced by the vast solar magnetic fields.

During totality, it is the corona that defines the eclipse for many people, and it is only during this darkest part of a solar eclipse that you don't need special equipment or eye protection to marvel at it.

The extent of the corona
can be seen during a
total solar eclipse

SOLAR **SAFETY**

Solar observing is the one time that astronomy poses a real risk of physical injury. Here's how to do it safely...

SOLAR PROJECTION
All you need is a piece of white card, onto which you project the image of the Sun from your scope or binoculars. You could also fix another piece around the front end of the scope to create a shadow around the projection. Good for eclipses and sunspots.
Cost: free

CARDBOARD SUN PROJECTOR
These kits are simply a small telescope and mirror that projects an image of the Sun onto a white screen on the inside of the box. It will show much the same views as the solar projection setup – great if you don't have a scope.
Cost: from £49

SOLAR FILTERS
These glass or film coverings fit completely over the light-gathering front end of the scope, stopping all heat and virtually all light from the Sun entering the scope. Good for viewing sunspots and granulation.
Cost: film filters from £40, glass filters from £70

PERSONAL SOLAR TELESCOPE
The Personal Solar Telescope (PST) is made to reveal one specific wavelength of light and can show much more than your naked eye will see with film or glass filters. Good for prominences, active regions, filaments and faculae.
Cost: from £480

SIGHTS ON THE SUN

YOU'LL NEED A FILTER TO VIEW THE SUN SAFELY AND SEE THE INCREDIBLE ACTIVITY ON OUR NEAREST STAR. HERE'S WHAT TO LOOK OUT FOR

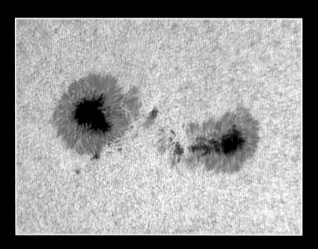

‹ SUNSPOTS
These features usually appear in pairs and are caused by magnetism, which draws away energy. Their resulting lower temperature makes these regions appear dark.

LIMB DARKENING
The photosphere is translucent, so when you look at its centre you're peering deep into the hotter, brighter part. This is why it appears lighter than it does at the edges.

PHOTOSPHERE
The light from the Sun is given off here. Its temperature is around 6,000°C and it is home to sunspots.

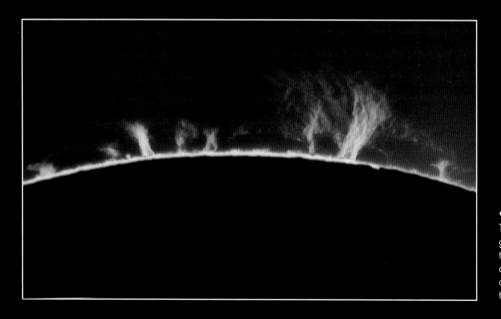

‹ PROMINENCES
These are concentrations of gas, associated with sunspots, that move up from the chromosphere. In just an hour, active prominences can shoot to heights of ⁄50,000km.

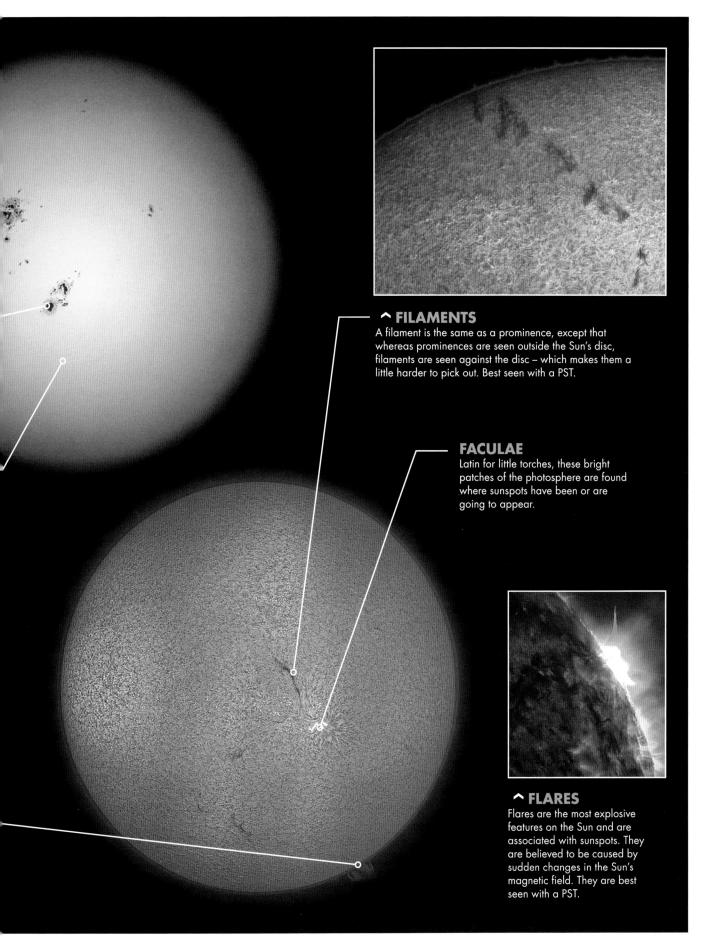

⌃ FILAMENTS

A filament is the same as a prominence, except that whereas prominences are seen outside the Sun's disc, filaments are seen against the disc – which makes them a little harder to pick out. Best seen with a PST.

FACULAE

Latin for little torches, these bright patches of the photosphere are found where sunspots have been or are going to appear.

⌃ FLARES

Flares are the most explosive features on the Sun and are associated with sunspots. They are believed to be caused by sudden changes in the Sun's magnetic field. They are best seen with a PST.

SOLAR ECLIPSES

THE ANCIENT CHINESE THOUGHT SOLAR ECLIPSES WERE THE SUN BEING EATEN BY A DRAGON. TODAY WE KNOW EXACTLY WHAT CAUSES THEM – AND WHERE TO GET THE BEST VIEWS

One of the most breathtaking astronomical events you can witness is a total eclipse of the Sun, also known as a total solar eclipse. Not only is it an experience you'll never forget, but it also shows the Solar System in motion through the fortunate alignment of three astronomical bodies.

The first object is our planet, the Earth, which slowly orbits the second object, the Sun. The third object in the equation is the Moon. We get an eclipse when the Sun, Moon and Earth are temporarily aligned.

The next total eclipse takes place this year on 13 November, but totality will only be seen from Cairns, Australia. It will, however, be seen as a partial eclipse in central Chile, and areas of New Zealand, such as Auckland and Christchurch. It

won't be visible from the UK, though, so you'll have to travel if you want to see it.

On Earth we're really rather lucky that the Moon is just the right size and orbits at just the right distance to make total solar eclipses possible. You may wonder how they happen at all since the Sun is so much bigger than the Moon. Well, due to one of the most amazing coincidences in nature, even though the Moon is 400 times smaller than the Sun, the Sun

is around 400 times further away. As a result, the two objects can appear to be the same size.

However, we don't get a total solar eclipse every time the Moon moves between Earth and the Sun. The lunar orbit is tilted, so that it sometimes

CASTING **SHADOWS**

See total coverage of the Sun in the umbra

During a total solar eclipse, if you're in the 'umbra' you'll see the entire Sun slowly covered by the Moon and get the full glory of totality. There's also an area around the umbra called the 'penumbra', where the shadow isn't quite so dark. On the ground this forms a large circular zone where you see more and more of the Sun the further you get from the umbra until you don't see an eclipse at all. So whenever people in one location see a total eclipse, those in a large surrounding area will see a partial eclipse. There are a maximum of five solar eclipses in any given year.

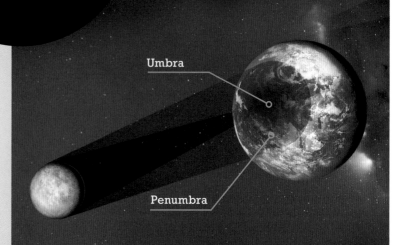

The cone-shaped shadow of the Moon cast by the Sun creates an umbra and penumbra on Earth

Left-right: The Moon takes a small bite out of the Sun; a 'diamond ring' effect is observed; the total eclipse; the 'diamond ring' appears again; and a final, diminishing bite

HOW TO SEE AN **ECLIPSE**

Three ways to see it

PINHOLE
A safe way of viewing an eclipse is with two pieces of card. Make a small hole in one and hold the other so that the Sun is projected onto it. You can then watch as events unfold.

PROJECTING
You can set up binoculars on a tripod to capture an eclipse. Hold a piece of card away from the eyepieces so the sunlight is projected onto it, then watch the Moon cover up the Sun.

ECLIPSE GLASSES
You can now buy safe eclipse viewers that you wear just like sunglasses. They cut out all harmful ultraviolet and infrared rays and 99.9 per cent of the Sun's visible light.

passes above or below the Sun. And because the Moon's orbit isn't circular but elliptical, like an oval, when it is furthest from us and an eclipse occurs the Moon is too small to cover the Sun completely. We then see an 'annular eclipse', in which a thin ring of sunlight can be seen circling the Moon.

SUN BLOCKED
When we witness a total solar eclipse it means that we are in the shadow of the Moon and, as the Sun is the bigger object, it makes the shadow of the Moon cone-shaped (see 'Casting shadows', left).

This shadow cone starts out as big as the diameter of the Moon at 3,476km (2,160 miles), but by the time it reaches the Earth the shadow is much smaller – the biggest it can get is about 300km (190 miles) in diameter. If you're lucky enough to be within the zone of the shadow, you'll see darkness descend as the shadow sweeps across the planet.

During an eclipse the Moon will cover the Sun entirely for seven minutes 31 seconds at most, but you'll probably see a 'totality' lasting somewhere between two and four minutes. If you're not within the 300km circle of the shadow cone, however, you'll only see a partial eclipse because the Moon covers up less of the Sun as you move further away from the track of totality.

Do, however, be careful! Due to the intense light from the Sun, a total eclipse is dangerous to look at. The only time when it's safe to look directly at the eclipse is during the few minutes of totality when the Moon completely covers the Sun. For the rest of the event you must protect your eyes from the Sun's glare. Take appropriate care and you can fully enjoy this marvel of celestial mechanics.

LUNAR ECLIPSES

WHILE SOLAR ECLIPSES ZOOM ACROSS THE FACE OF EARTH, SPECTACULAR RED LUNAR ECLIPSES ARE MUCH SLOWER SO SIT BACK, RELAX AND ENJOY THE TRANQUIL PROCEEDINGS

Look up at the Moon at certain times of the year and you'll be able to witness the motion of the Solar System on a truly grand scale. There's nothing quite like watching a lunar eclipse as the Sun, Earth and Moon become perfectly aligned.

There are three types of lunar eclipse, the most exciting of which is a total lunar eclipse. The other two types are partial and penumbral lunar eclipses, which we'll come to later.

Total lunar eclipses can only happen at full Moon when the Sun, Earth and Moon are lined up in space. However, most months the Moon moves above or below Earth's shadow, which is why eclipses don't happen every time the Moon is full. They occur when the Moon travels into Earth's shadow during full Moon. Slowly, the Moon approaches the exact opposite side of the sky to where the Sun is and as it does so Earth blocks out more and more sunlight from reaching it. As the Moon travels into Earth's shadow, the left side of the Moon gradually darkens until the Moon is totally covered – totality.

MECHANICS OF A **LUNAR ECLIPSE**

All the lunar eclipse effects that happen, such as darkening and colour changes, are due to Earth blocking off sunlight to the Moon. Only sunlight that has been bent (refracted) by Earth's atmosphere reaches the Moon (shown by the bent line in the diagram). When the Sun's rays intercept Earth they form two zones of shadow: the penumbra, where some of the Sun is always seen; and the umbra, where the Sun is completely hidden by Earth. The eclipse appears to begin in earnest when the Moon starts to move into this umbra region and its surface begins to darken, before turning an unusual orange-red colour.

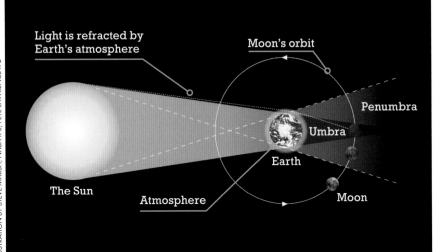

Light is refracted by
Earth's atmosphere

Moon's orbit

Penumbra

Umbra

Earth

The Sun

Atmosphere

Moon

Because the Sun is much bigger than Earth, it splits our planet's shadow into two parts: the darkest, called the umbra, and a lighter outer ring, called the penumbra (see the diagram, left). When the Moon is in the umbra, no direct light from the Sun reaches it, whereas in the penumbra it is partially lit by direct sunlight.

Only light that has been bent inwards by Earth's atmosphere can make it to the Moon when it is in the umbral shadow. The atmosphere filters out blue light, but leaves red light, which gives the Moon a strange orange-brown colour during totality.

As the Moon goes into eclipse and dims, the sky gets darker too. You may not have realised how bright a full Moon can be. It lights up the sky around it with a blue haze, out of which only the brighter stars are visible. During a total lunar eclipse, the darker Moon means that the fainter stars can come out and we end up with the eerie sight of a deep-red Moon surrounded by twinkling stars.

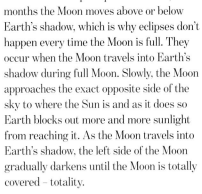

ILLUSTRATION BY STEVE MARSH, NASA X 3, PETE LAWRENCE X 2

Watch as the full Moon starts to darken, before becoming orange-red as it is completely covered by Earth's shadow

This is what you'd see if you were on the surface of the Moon during a total lunar eclipse. As the Moon moves into Earth's shadow to totality at stage 4, our planet's atmosphere glows red

1

2

3

4

The beauty of a lunar eclipse is that it is visible wherever you are on the night-side of Earth. The Moon can be in shadow for over an hour and a half, so the whole thing is quite a gentle process and you won't need any special equipment to see it.

RED MOON AT NIGHT

As for the other eclipse types: a partial eclipse is when only part of the Moon travels through the dark umbral shadow. It can be quite noticeable though, as you can see for yourself by watching the next partial event on 25 April 2013. You may even have seen a penumbral eclipse without noticing. This is when the Moon only passes through the lighter part of Earth's shadow; sunlight still reaches the Moon, so you only see a slight dimming. You can see one on 28 November 2012. But if it's a total lunar eclipse you want to see, there's a bit of a wait sadly: the next one visible in Europe isn't until 28 September 2015!

THE DANJON SCALE

The Danjon Scale, named after its creator, the French astronomer André-Louis Danjon, describes how dark the Moon gets during a total lunar eclipse.

It measures the darkness of an eclipse from L0 through to L4. All lunar eclipses are very different in colour, going from light orange to dark brown. This is because during an eclipse, the Moon is only lit by light that has passed through Earth's atmosphere. So the colour will depend on how much dust, volcanic ash and water vapour is in the atmosphere to affect the sunlight's path.

The eclipse in 1884, after the huge volcanic eruption of Krakatoa, was so dark that the Moon could only just be made out, such was the amount of dust in the atmosphere.

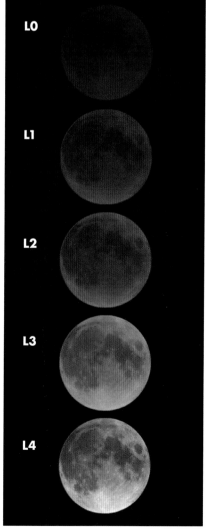

L0

L1

L2

L3

L4

THE PLANETS
PART 1 INTRODUCTION

SCIENTISTS USE SPACE PROBES TO STUDY THE OTHER MEMBERS OF THE SOLAR SYSTEM, YET THERE'S STILL SOMETHING SPECIAL ABOUT SEEING A PLANET WITH YOUR OWN EYES

PLANETS IN MOTION

DAY
The time it takes for a planet to spin once on its axis relative to another object. For Earth, relative to the Sun, the day is 24 hours long. But relative to the stars it's 23 hours 56 minutes and 4 seconds because the Sun moves against this fixed background.

ORBIT
A planet's orbit is the circular or elliptical path it makes around the Sun.

YEAR
The time it takes for a planet to orbit once around the Sun. One year for Venus is 224.7 Earth days, while one year for Neptune is 164.8 Earth years.

Out there in space is a pretty average star about halfway through its life, shining away with a nice even temperament – our Sun. I can say all this because, after all, we wouldn't be here if our star wasn't so calm and collected.

The Sun isn't actually stationary, but travels around (or orbits) the centre of our Galaxy about every 250 million years – known to those in the trade as one galactic year. Of course, the Sun is not alone on its journey; its gravity pulls a rag-tag bunch of comets, asteroids, moons and planets along for the ride. All together these take on the title of the Solar System.

The number of planets there are has changed over time. Currently there are eight bodies recognised as planets and five objects classed as dwarf planets, including Pluto, Eris and Ceres.

Pluto lost its planetary status in 2006, after other similar (and some larger) objects were found where it orbits. But to meet today's definition of a planet, as well as being rounded by its own gravitational force and in orbit round the Sun, a body has to have cleared its orbit other objects its size, which Pluto hasn't done .

OUR SOLAR SYSTEM

All the planets move in the same anticlockwise direction around the Sun, if we take Earth's north pole as an arbitrary reference of 'up'. Several of them are big enough and close enough to Earth to be a worthwhile target for your telescope, but before we get to that, let's take a moment to examine, compare and contrast the planets some more.

The Sun's gravity 'well' is immense – imagine a great bowling ball creating a dip in a trampoline. The planets are like marbles rolling along inside this dip around the bowling ball Sun. The closer you are to the Sun, the stronger its pull of gravity and the faster you have to move to keep from being pulled into solar destruction. By the same logic, the further you travel from the Sun, the less its pull of gravity and the slower you travel in your orbit.

Earth takes one year to travel around the Sun, but closer Mercury takes only 88 Earth days. Looking at the comparative speed of each planet, we find Earth

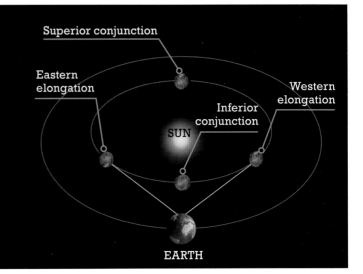

INFERIOR PLANETS

The two planets that are closer to the Sun than Earth are Mercury and Venus, and together they are known as the inferior planets. Due to the nature of their orbits, the best time to observe them is when they are at their farthest angular distance from the Sun, a position astronomers call elongation.

At these times, the planets are only half lit by the Sun, but after this they swing back into the solar glare, where they become less visible. For example, when Mercury and Venus are at eastern elongation, they set after the Sun in the evening; when they're at western elongation they rise before the Sun in the morning.

The Sun interferes with our views of the inferior planets twice during their orbits: when it, Earth and the planet are lined up. When a planet is between Earth and the Sun, it's at inferior conjunction; when it's on the far side of the Sun, it's said to be at superior conjunction.

Superior conjunction

Eastern elongation

Western elongation

Inferior conjunction

SUN

EARTH

PLANETARY ORBITS

Pluto (dwarf planet)
Eris (dwarf planet)
Neptune
Uranus
Venus   Mercury
Earth
Mars
Ceres (dwarf planet)
Jupiter
Saturn
The Sun

moves at an average of 29.8km/s (107,280km/h), while Mercury moves at a speedy average of 47.4km/s (170,640km/h) along its orbit. Compare that with the furthest current planetary object, Eris, which travels a slow mean speed of just 3.4km/s (12,240km/h). All this speed, or lack of it, affects how a planet moves across the night sky as seen from Earth's surface. Whereas Saturn crawls around the sky, barely moving among the starry skies, Mercury's fast pace means it shifts considerably day by day.

This is what the gravity of the Sun does, but there's also its light to consider. We see the planets because the Sun lights them up. Their brightness is due to many things, including their actual distance from the Sun, the distance they are from your eye, and their size, composition and colour. The brightest planet of all as seen from Earth is Venus, also known as the Evening or Morning Star due to the brilliance of its appearance.

SUPERIOR PLANETS

All the planets further from the Sun than Earth are called the superior planets. These don't present the same problems for observers as Mercury and Venus, speeding their way round the Sun, and so they can be visible all night long if they are in the right place. When any of these planets line up with the Earth on the far side of the Sun, they are said to be in conjunction, and are not observable as they rise with the Sun in the day.

The best time to observe the superior planets is when they are close to Earth. This happens at around the time called opposition, when another lining-up takes place. This time the planet is on the opposite side of the sky to the Sun, so we are presented with a fully illuminated disc: visually it's close to or at its biggest and brightest. This is the time to get out your telescope and have a good old eyeball – you'll be able to make out the most amount of detail.

Conjunction
SUN
Opposition
EARTH

THE PLANETS

PART 2 TERRESTRIAL WORLDS

MERCURY, VENUS AND MARS ARE THE CLOSEST ROCKY PLANETS TO EARTH, AND ALL WILL GIVE YOU MEMORABLE VIEWS IF YOU KNOW WHEN TO LOOK

Thinking back to 'ye olde dayes', there were no space probes visiting the planets. Telescopes were able to reveal that Venus was covered in cloud, but it was a guess as to what was underneath: both jungle and seas were respectable ideas. I wonder what these pioneering astronomers would think of our current knowledge, together with all the stunning images that go with it.

Today, in our information-rich world, most people know the basics about the planets. It's easy to forget the angst the early astronomers suffered due to their serious lack of reliable, scientific information.

In part one, I gave a general overview of our entire planetary system, giving you the bigger view of how the planets move together, helped along by that fine force of gravity. Now that you're familiar with the workings of the Solar System, it's time to take a look at its planets in more detail.

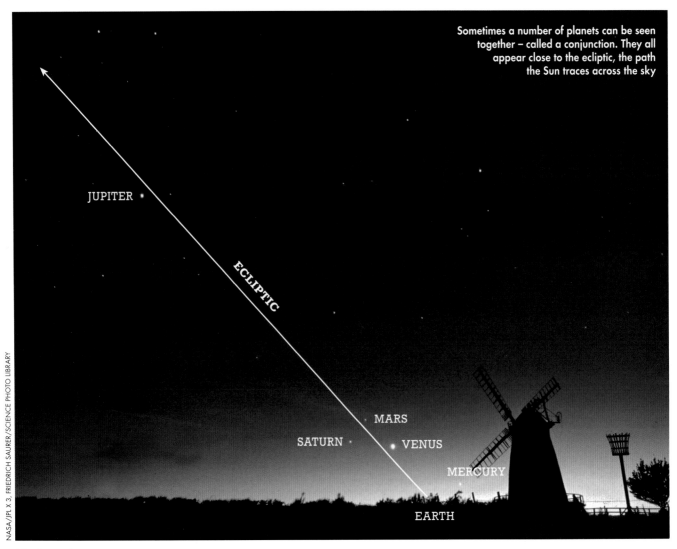

Sometimes a number of planets can be seen together – called a conjunction. They all appear close to the ecliptic, the path the Sun traces across the sky

JUPITER

ECLIPTIC

MARS

SATURN · VENUS

MERCURY

EARTH

MERCURY

Mean distance from the Sun:
58 million km
Rotation period: 59 days
Orbital period: 88 days
Diameter: 4,900km
Gravity (Earth=1): 0.38
Surface temperature:
350°C (day), –170°C (night)
Number of moons: 0

This small world is a real challenge to observe for a variety of reasons. It's a fast mover, travelling around the Sun four times quicker than Earth, so don't expect it to hang about in any part of the sky for very long – it only stays around one week at a time.

Mercury's orbit is a fairly eccentric oval shape, and it's on a bit of a tilt too, which means there are better times to view it than others: spring evenings and autumn mornings. If that's not tricky enough, you only have a relatively short observation window on any day you choose to look, as Mercury never goes very far from the Sun.

In spring, start looking for the planet 30 minutes after sunset, after which point you'll have about another 45 minutes to see it. Autumn gives you a longer view, and you can start looking about 1 hour and 45 minutes before sunrise, but that does mean getting up exceedingly early.

Mercury and Venus are worlds apart in that Venus is easy to see most of the time. The brilliance of its appearance makes for one of the finest naked-eye views in the evening or dawn skies, especially if the crescent Moon is nearby.

Because the 'Cytherean' (as opposed to the strictly incorrect adjective 'Venusian') orbit is slower than Mercury's, it can be visible for months on end, and sometimes for up to three hours after sunset or before sunrise.

When Venus is at its brightest, it becomes the third-brightest object in the sky, only beaten by the Moon and the Sun. This is caused by sunlight reflecting off its bright white carbon-dioxide clouds, and has led to Venus being called the 'Evening Star' or 'Morning Star' depending on when it appears. Venus can come very close to Earth, plus it's rather big, meaning that it's a good target for binoculars, through which you can easily see its larger phases.

VENUS

Mean distance from the Sun:
108 million km
Rotation period: 243 days
Orbital period: 225 days
Diameter: 12,100km
Gravity (Earth=1): 0.903
Surface temperature:
480°C
Number of moons: 0

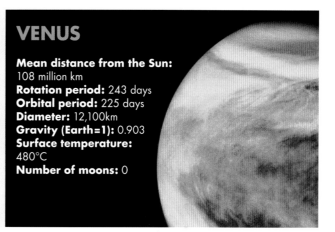

MARS

Mean distance from the Sun:
228 million km
Rotation period: 24 hrs 37 min
Orbital period: 687 days
Diameter: 6,800km
Gravity (Earth=1): 0.380
Surface temperature: –23°C
Number of moons: 2

Our final main terrestrial, or rocky, planet differs from Mercury and Venus in that its position in the Solar System affects the way in which it is visible. Mars orbits further from the Sun than the Earth and can be 'up' from sunset until sunrise.

This happens when the planet is at opposition, when Mars is on exactly the opposite side of the sky to the Sun. The Sun, Earth and Mars are lined up in space, with Earth in the middle. This leads to the planet being at its highest and brightest at midnight, as this is when Mars is near its closest point to Earth. The weeks around opposition are often when the colour of the Red Planet becomes truly apparent.

This is the best time to view Mars with a telescope. You'll be able to see lighter, pale-reddish areas, the bright white of the ice caps, and darker patches, which it used to be thought were Martian 'cities'. Oppositions of Mars happen once every 26 months, with the last one in March 2012.

CERES – DWARF PLANET

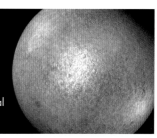

After you pass Mars there are hundreds of thousands of smaller objects in an area commonly known as the Asteroid Belt. The first one discovered was thought to be a new planet – its name was Ceres and it turned out to be the largest of these objects. Unfortunately, it was still rather small, which meant it didn't keep its planetary status for long. Then, in 2006, its classification changed again when the International Astronomical Union gave Ceres the status of dwarf planet. As it's such a small object, you'll need binoculars to find it.

THE PLANETS
PART 3 GAS GIANTS

BEYOND THE ORBIT OF MARS YOU'LL FIND SOME OF THE MOST EXCITING AND HOSTILE ENVIRONMENTS IN THE SOLAR SYSTEM. HERE WE TAKE A LOOK AT JUPITER AND THE PLANETS BEYOND

Following the small planetary hops within the warm inner Solar System in part two, we now take a trip across the vast stretches of colder space to the outer worlds. From Jupiter onwards not only is it colder, but the planets also travel at an increasingly slow pace owing to less gravitational pull from the Sun. This can be observed from their tiny weekly movements across the sky. Neptune, for example, travels so slowly that, during an average human lifetime of 75 years, it won't have completed even half a Neptunian year – it will still have the other half of its journey around the Sun to go.

JUPITER

Mean distance from the Sun:
778 million km
Rotation period: 9 hrs 55 min
Orbital period: 11.9 years
Diameter: 142,800km
Gravity (Earth=1): 2.69
Mean atmospheric temperature: –153°C
Number of moons: 63

Jupiter's distinctive Great Red Spot and bands are clearly visible through a small telescope, inset

Jupiter is a fine observing target. With a good pair of binoculars the first things you'll notice are its main moons: Io, Europa, Ganymede and Callisto. With a telescope you'll see a slightly squashed sphere. This is due to its fast spinning 'day' of just under 10 hours, which causes the equator to bulge outwards and the poles to flatten. Jupiter's cloudy atmosphere will be revealed as dark bands separated by white zones. The longer you look, the more features appear, so keep an eye out for spots, wisps and kinks. The most famous feature is, of course, the Great Red Spot, a storm that changes shape, size and colour over time, often appearing quite greyish.

At around the time of opposition – when the planet is opposite to the Sun in the sky and closest to Earth – Jupiter becomes a sparkly night-time beacon. Shining at a maximum magnitude of –2.8, it appears as an unmistakable 'star' that will certainly catch your attention. The next few opposition dates for Jupiter are 3 December 2012, 6 January 2014 and 7 February 2015. These are the best times to see the planet shine. Being closer to Earth means Jupiter is at its largest appearance-wise – great for anyone who owns binoculars or a telescope. Don't expect to see all of its big satellites though, as they could be in front of, or behind, the planet.

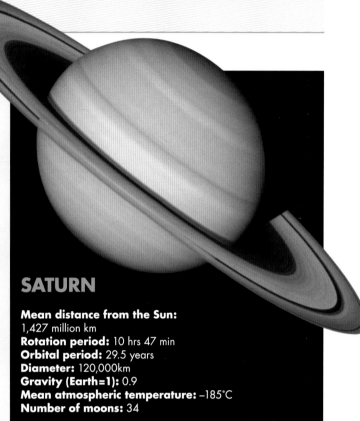

Saturn is farther away from the Sun and smaller than Jupiter, so it's fainter and its maximum brightness varies more, from +0.8 to –3.3. Its variable brightness is due to the way the rings are tilted and how much sunlight is reflected back our way. Saturn is not so bright when the rings are edge-on to us, but its brightness increases over 7.5 years as the rings open up to observers on Earth. Then it fades again over the same period.

If you're wondering why this takes 7.5 years, it's a quarter of the time Saturn takes to go around the Sun. Oppositions of Saturn over the next few years occur on 28 April 2013, 11 May 2014 and 23 May 2015, when the Ringed Planet will be brightest.

The best way of understanding Saturn's tilting effect is to go out and look at the planet – it really is one of the telescopic marvels of the Solar System. It doesn't matter if you have a small scope: the sight of a world surrounded by rings is amazing. I've seen Saturn through large and small scopes and it's actually the little ones that get my vote every time. The view of this tiny ringed world hanging in a large, inky black field of view is magical. Larger scopes will start to show detail in the rings and on the planet.

Saturn is especially magical when its rings are tilted towards Earth

SATURN

Mean distance from the Sun: 1,427 million km
Rotation period: 10 hrs 47 min
Orbital period: 29.5 years
Diameter: 120,000km
Gravity (Earth=1): 0.9
Mean atmospheric temperature: –185°C
Number of moons: 34

URANUS

Mean distance from the Sun: 2.8 billion km
Rotation period: 17 hrs 14 min
Orbital period: 84 years
Diameter: 50,800km
Gravity (Earth=1): 0.89
Mean atmospheric temperature: –214°C
Number of moons: 27

Uranus's greenish colour is clear through a small telescope

Sadly, not all the planets are exciting. Uranus doesn't have much going for it, whether you use your eyes, a pair of binoculars or a telescope. Turning your head upwards, you can just see this gaseous world as a very faint star at the limits of visibility (around mag. +5.6). You won't see much from anywhere with light pollution – the sky has to be very black indeed. The view does improve a little through a telescope, showing a greenish speck.

PLUTO AND ERIS

Pluto and Eris are two examples of objects now defined as 'dwarf planets'. Since 2006, the Solar System has had eight planets and five dwarf planets after 76 years of there being nine. Included in dwarf planets are some of the more interesting 'larger' members of the swarm of rock and ice known as the Kuiper Belt – the remnant of planetary formation that lies beyond Neptune. This may turn out to be the most fascinating part of the Solar System, with its untouched, uncontaminated and unheated material billions of years old. NASA's New Horizons spacecraft will reach this mysterious region in 2015.

At around mag. +8° you need at least binoculars to see Neptune, and there isn't much else to say. I've viewed it through a telescope, and so ticked it off the list, but this tiny looking 'star', maybe with a hint of blue, is not as spectacular as its larger compatriots. If you have a very large scope it's worth catching a glimpse of Neptune's largest moon, Triton (mag. +13.5). However, if I were you, I'd invest my efforts in observing some of the more accessible sights the Milky Way has to offer.

NEPTUNE

Mean distance from the Sun: 4.5 billion km
Rotation period: 16 hrs 6 min
Orbital period: 164.8 years
Diameter: 48,600km
Gravity (Earth=1): 1.14
Mean atmospheric temperature: –225°C
Number of moons: 13

Through a large telescope, Neptune has a hint of blue

OBSERVING JUPITER'S MOONS

THE SOLAR SYSTEM'S BIGGEST PLANET ALSO HAS THE MOST MOONS, FOUR OF WHICH ARE EASY TO SEE

The Solar System is truly an incredible place, but one world in particular stands out and truly deserves the title King of the Planets: Jupiter. It is grandiose in all respects. Not only is it the largest of the planets – it would take 1,321 Earths to fill the volume of Jupiter – it's also more than likely that it keeps the largest entourage of moons.

It's the massive gravitational effect of Jupiter that does the trick, attracting more than 100 moons into orbit around the planet at the latest estimate. Many of these

satellites are fairly small and can't be observed from Earth, but the biggest four are easy to spot with just a small pair of binoculars.

A minimum size pair for spotting these four moons would be 7x50s, which magnify what your eyes see seven times and have front lenses that are 50mm in diameter. You can certainly catch glimpses of these Galilean moons (named after Galileo, who first observed them) with hand-held binoculars, but your view will be much

improved by resting the binoculars on a wall or fence, or even attaching them to a tripod with an inexpensive bracket. With binoculars though, Jupiter itself will not appear as anything more than a large, slightly oval-shaped disc.

MOONWATCH

The next step in viewing Jupiter is to use a small telescope – one with a front lens 3 to 6 inches in diameter. As this gathers more light, it can magnify the view more, so the

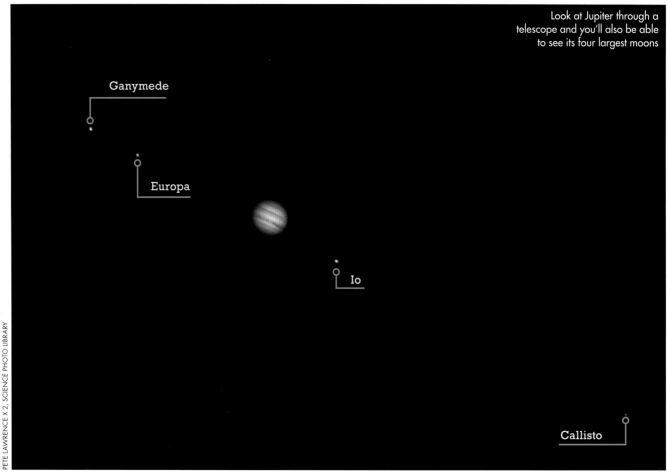

Look at Jupiter through a telescope and you'll also be able to see its four largest moons

Ganymede

Europa

Io

Callisto

THE GALILEAN MOONS

IO
Diameter: 3,640km

The tremendous gravitational pull of Jupiter on this innermost of the four Galilean moons, together with its closeness to the planet, means Io whizzes round Jupiter in just 1.75 Earth days. This fast orbital speed is easily seen in a small telescope: it visibly shifts position in just a few hours. Physically, Io is the most volcanic place in the entire Solar System. The whole world is covered in sulphurous lava flows and volcanoes erupting in plumes more than 500km high.

GANYMEDE
Diameter: 5,260km

The third major moon out from the planet is not only Jupiter's biggest, but it is also the largest moon in the entire Solar System. This is a world with a cold ice surface, a large warm ice (possibly water) mantle, a rocky interior and a liquid iron core. It measures a tremendous 5,260km across, which is bigger than Mercury. Indeed, if Ganymede was released into space, it would be classed as a planet.

EUROPA
Diameter: 3,140km

The second Galilean moon out from Jupiter, Europa, should theoretically be visible with the naked eye since it shines at mag +5.3. But Jupiter's overwhelming brightness makes it difficult to separate the moon from the planet. Europa's brightness is due to its surface being smooth and icy. Scientists suspect that underneath is a liquid water ocean, leaving open the possibility that life may lurk in the depths.

CALLISTO
Diameter: 4,820km

The last of the four giant Galilean satellites is Callisto. It is the third largest of the Solar System, after Titan, the biggest of Saturn's moons. Callisto ranks as one of the most cratered worlds known – its entire icy, ancient surface is covered with impact craters that date right back to the time of the early Solar System, when the moon formed. Like Europa, it is thought that beneath the surface may lie a watery ocean.

Moons will appear brighter and fill more of the field of view.

Don't necessarily expect to see all four, however: as the moons travel around the planet they may be behind or in front of Jupiter when you're looking.

It's by using a larger scope with a front lens over 6 inches in diameter that you really start to see detail on the planet itself: not only the darker belts and lighter

With larger scopes you can see shadows of the moons on Jupiter's disc

zones, but features within the gaseous atmosphere as well. At this level of detail, observers can also see the occasional dark spot caused by the moons casting their shadows onto Jupiter's atmosphere. The joy of Jupiter is that whatever your level of equipment, there's always something to see.

The best times to see the planet is when it's at opposition. This is when Jupiter is positioned directly opposite the Sun in the sky from our point of view, and so it's really bright.

The next time Jupiter's at opposition will be 3 December 2012. The best views will be when the planet reaches its highest point in the sky, due south around midnight. It will stand out near the constellation of Taurus. After that, Jupiter will find its way back to opposition on 5 January 2014 (when it'll be visible around 2.30am in Gemini) and on 6 February 2015, near midnight.

Happy observing, and remember – what seems like an easy amateur target today was once a hugely significant sight that made history at the start of the 17th century. When Galileo first saw Jupiter's moons, it proved scientifically that Earth was not unique and wasn't at the centre of the Universe.

OBSERVING SATURN'S MOONS

NEXT TIME YOU OBSERVE THE RINGED PLANET, MAKE SURE YOU TAKE IN ITS MANY MOONS

Looking at Saturn through a telescope is a glorious sight. However, Saturn is best viewed when the ringed planet is at opposition – when its orbit brings it to its closest point to Earth. The next time you can get a 'close-up' view of Saturn like this will be when it's next at opposition on 28 April 2013, then again on 11 May 2014.

On these dates Saturn will be at its biggest and brightest in the sky – although the 'biggest' part is only apparent through a telescope. This applies to Saturn's moons too, which will also be at their optimum brightness for observing. The planet and

its moons' visibility during this period, along with the fact that the angle at which its rings can be seen varies, gives you the perfect excuse to get out and view this amazing world.

Saturn has 62 known moons, but only seven are visible. Due to its sheer size, the easiest of Saturn's satellites to see is Titan. This moon has a diameter of 5,150km (3,200 miles), which makes it bigger than the planet Mercury. In the moon rankings, it's the second largest in the Solar System, only beaten by Jupiter's Ganymede. It's also the only moon with a substantial atmosphere.

When you're gazing at it through your scope, you're not actually looking at Titan's surface but at its nitrogen-rich cloud tops. In terms of brightness, Titan can reach mag. +8.4, putting it well within the reach of binoculars, while with a small telescope you'll have no trouble seeing it at all.

Don't forget that just because you see a small point of light near Saturn, it doesn't mean you're looking at one of its moons. As planets travel through space they often drift in front of faint background stars, so it's important to know what is a moon and what isn't. You can separate your moons

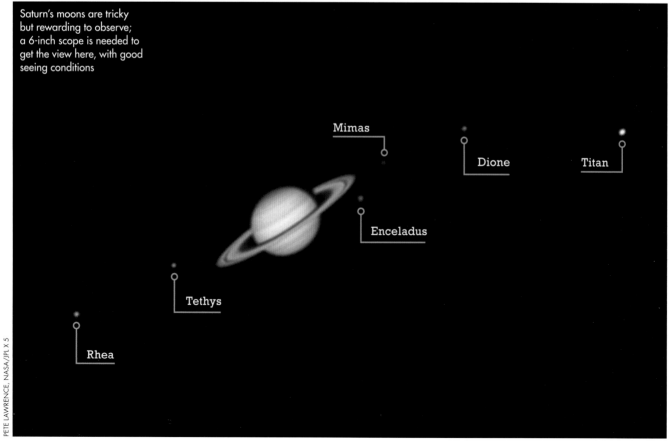

Saturn's moons are tricky but rewarding to observe; a 6-inch scope is needed to get the view here, with good seeing conditions

Mimas

Dione

Titan

Enceladus

Tethys

Rhea

SATURN'S TOP 5 MOONS TO OBSERVE

TITAN
The largest of Saturn's moons has a 16-day orbit. At its farthest, you'll find it about five of Saturn's ring diameters from the planet, with a brightest visual magnitude of +8.4, which makes it visible in good binoculars. This large moon makes up over 96 per cent of the mass of everything in orbit around the planet.

RHEA
The second largest moon of Saturn and currently the 20th catalogued in distance out from the planet. It makes an orbit in 4.5 days, reaching just under two ring diameters from Saturn. The visual magnitude is +9.7, making Rhea an easy target for a 3-inch refractor telescope. The moon is covered with an icy surface.

IAPETUS
This is the third largest and most distant of the main moons of Saturn. Its 79-day orbit takes it out to 12 ring diameters from the planet. The visual magnitude ranges from +10.1 to +11.9, so Iapetus needs about a 6-inch scope to see it at its darkest. Unlike the other, larger moons, Iapetus has quite an inclined orbit.

DIONE
This moon orbits up to 1.5 ring diameters from Saturn, over 2.7 days. Its visual magnitude of +10.4 makes it visible on dark nights with a 3-inch refractor. This is the densest of the moons, which means that it may have a large rocky core. Two smaller moons, Helene and Polydeuces, share the same orbit as Dione.

TETHYS
This moon orbits about one ring diameter away from the planet and takes 1.9 days to do so. It has a visual magnitude of +10.3 and so can be seen in a 3-inch refractor. Tethys has a great canyon that stretches three-quarters of the way round the moon, and it is believed to be composed of water-ice.

---

from your stars using planetarium software to check your observing field before you go out. The other alternative is a moon locator diagram. For an explanation of what these are and how to use them see 'Moon diagrams', right.

MEET THE FAMILY
After Titan, the next brightest moon is Rhea, which shines at mag. +9.7. This is quite a substantial drop in brightness, but Rhea will look its best through a 6-inch scope or larger, as will the rest of the fainter, visible moons.

There are seven of Saturn's moons within the grasp of a 6-inch scope. After Titan and Rhea, in decreasing brightness, come Tethys at mag. +10.3, Dione at mag +10.4, Enceladus at mag +11.8 and Iapetus.

The last moon mentioned is a very interesting world indeed. Its unusual nature became apparent when it was discovered by the Italian astronomer Giovanni Cassini in 1671. He first saw the moon on the western side of Saturn but found it missing on a later search, when it should have been on the eastern side.

It wasn't until 34 years later, when telescopes had improved, that Cassini finally saw Iapetus to the east, because when it's here it's almost two magnitudes

fainter. This is why it had been impossible to see it before.

Cassini deduced, correctly, that this was because the moon has one very bright hemisphere and one very dark one, and is also tidally locked to Saturn. This means, like our Moon, it always shows the same face to its planet. It follows that we see a different part of Iapetus from our Earthly viewpoint when it is to the east or west of Saturn. As a result, Iapetus varies between mag. +10.1 and mag +11.9. However, the faintness trophy goes to the moon Mimas, which at mag. +12.9, needs perfect viewing conditions without any light pollution to be able to see it comfortably. Moving up to an 8-inch aperture will improve your chances of seeing this distant world.

To catch Saturn and its moons at their best, ideally you want to be out observing at opposition, although the planet will show for a month before that exact date, getting gradually higher each night. On the actual day of opposition, Saturn will be in the sky all night moving up towards its highest point in the sky, which is due south.

The planet will still be visible for about a month after its opposition date too, although its height in the sky decreases gradually until it sinks below the horizon and is no longer visible.

MOON DIAGRAMS
One of the best ways of plotting the positions of Saturn's moons is with a diagram that looks a bit like a double helix. The orbit of each of Saturn's moons is represented by a line curving either side of a central vertical strip, which represents Saturn. An inner moon's line weaves back and forth close to the central strip, while an outer moon's line swings out wider from the strip depicting Saturn's movement. Dates are plotted down the diagram and you simply draw a horizontal line across for the date you want to observe. Each moon's position with respect to Saturn is indicated where your line crosses a curve.

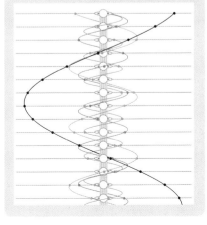

ESO; ROGER LYNDS/NAOAO/AURA/NSF; NASA KENNEDY SPACE CENTER (NASA-KSC); PETER STÄTTMAYER & ESO; M NEWBERRY & J MCGAHA;
ROBERT MCNAUGHT/SCIENCE PHOTO LIBRARY; GIOTTO (ESA) HMC MPAE; PAUL WOOTTON

TOP 5
COMETS

1 MCNAUGHT
Closest approach
to the Sun:
25.6 million km
Orbital period:
Millions of years
First spotted: Aug 2006
Best visibility: Jan 2007

2 IKEYA-SEKI
Closest approach
to the Sun:
1.2 million km
Orbital period:
1,056 and 877
years (due to break up)
First spotted: Sep 1965
Best visibility: Oct 1965

3 HALE-BOPP
Closest approach
to the Sun:
136.5 million km
Orbital period:
2,537 years
First spotted: Jul 1995
Best visibility: Apr 1996

4 WEST
Closest approach
to the Sun:
30 million km
Orbital period:
560,000 years
First spotted: Aug 1975
Best visibility: Mar 1976

5 HYAKUTAKE
Closest approach
to the Sun:
34.5 million km
Orbital period:
72,000 years
First spotted: Jan 1996
Best visibility: Mar 1996

COMETS

COMETS ARE THE LEAST PREDICTABLE CELESTIAL WANDERERS, BUT THEY'RE A HIGHLIGHT WHENEVER THEY ENTER THE SOLAR SYSTEM

We live in an age of high-tech telescopes and computer modelling, so there's something curiously reassuring about the way comets continue to do their own thing, regardless of what any experts say that they should be doing. It's this unpredictability that makes any cometary apparition a unique event. Will the comet be bright? How long will its tail be? The only thing you need to do to find out the answer is to take a look into the night sky, so long as you know when to do it.

Thankfully, with the help of the internet, you can keep right up to date with the latest discoveries, as well as predicted viewing opportunities and magnitudes. This is exactly what many of us did during December 2006 and January 2007 with the approach of Comet McNaught. All eyes were ready for what looked like a good naked-eye apparition. When it arrived it was much more, becoming a real evening showpiece and the brightest comet to grace our skies since Ikeya-Seki in 1965. But until McNaught actually whizzed by our planet, we knew nothing for sure. It's difficult to predict much about a particular comet because we're often missing key information about it. How big is it? How old is it? Has it visited the Sun lots of times before? What is it made of?

FLYING HIGH

Think of comets as big, dark, dirty snowballs. These icy balls get warmed by the Sun if they fly into the inner Solar System. Its heat melts and evaporates their ice, releasing gas and dust. This surrounds the nucleus of the snowball, making it invisible, so we cannot actually measure the comet's true size. We're not even totally sure where comets come from, although there is one leading theory about their origins being in the Oort Cloud and Kuiper Belt. It can take millions of years for

WHERE DO THEY COME FROM?

Comets are believed to be the leftover material from a nebula that collapsed to form the Sun and the Solar System. Forming a great halo around the Sun known as the Oort Cloud, at a distance of around one lightyear, these frozen bits are thought to generally stay out of the way in 'hibernation'.

However, passing stars can nudge one, two or maybe even thousands of comets our way. It is possible that some mass extinctions on Earth were caused by such events. Short-period comets, on the other hand are thought to originate in the Kuiper Belt.

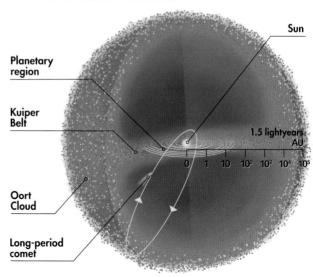

Sun
Planetary region
Kuiper Belt
Oort Cloud
Long-period comet
1.5 lightyears
AU
0   1   10   10²   10³   10⁴   10⁵

Although some comets have lost much of their lustre, others, like Comet McNaught, provide spectacular light shows

a comet to get here from the Oort Cloud, passing by Earth for just a day or two and producing a tremendous show before flying away again. However, some comets have their paths changed into smaller orbits around the Sun by the gravity of the gas giant planets, Jupiter in particular.

Those that travel with orbits lasting less than 200 years are known as short-period comets, while those with longer orbits are known as long-period comets. It has to be said that most of the short-period comets have been around the Sun so many times that they've lost much of their lustre: through a telescope they appear as little more than a fuzzy ball. However, even these can sometimes surprise us with an outburst, so do keep an eye out for these cheeky cosmic vagabonds.

DIRTY SNOWBALL

In March 1986, the Giotto probe imaged the nucleus of Halley's Comet. Giotto saw an odd, dark, potato-shaped object with outgassing caused by the warming Sun. It's funny to think that an icy ball a few kilometres across can create a roundish coma up to about 100,000km wide and, even more extraordinarily, a tail that can stretch from the Sun to the orbit of Mars.

CHASING THE TAIL

Comets generally have two visible tails: one composed of dust and one made of gas. It's the dust one that's the brighter of the two. Both tails appear when a comet is around 747,989,350km away from the Sun.

The dust tail is formed by solar radiation gently pushing on the particles released from the nucleus, while the gas tail comes from the interaction of released gas with the Sun's magnetic field.

Because a comet's speed is nowhere near that of the solar radiation, its tails always point away from the Sun, regardless of where the comet is in its orbit.

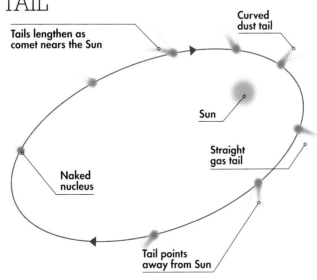

Tails lengthen as comet nears the Sun

Curved dust tail

Sun

Straight gas tail

Naked nucleus

Tail points away from Sun

OBSERVING TIPS

If you're up for a spot of meteor watching, then you'll need a full sky chart to help you find your way around the night sky. But here are a few other tips to make the task much more enjoyable and relaxing.

> Get things ready beforehand. If you are recording a shower you'll need pencils, paper, an accurate watch and a red torch so you don't ruin your dark adaptation.

> Deckchairs or sunloungers are perfect for a spot of meteor-gazing as you need to be comfortable while observing – but don't get so comfortable that you fall asleep!

> It will probably get cold, even in summer, so make sure you're wrapped up warm or at least have extra clothes nearby. Sleeping bags are always useful too.

> Darker skies are better for observing: try at least to have no streetlights in your view, and turn off all of your indoor house and outside security lights if you're in the garden.

> The clearer your horizon, the better: move away from trees or buildings because the more sky you can see, the more meteors you will be able to see.

SHOOTING STARS

WISHING ON A SHOOTING STAR IS ABOUT TO GET EASIER. DISCOVER THE SECRETS OF WHAT THEY ARE AND THE BEST WAYS TO SEE THEM

There you are on holiday, sitting in a bar overlooking the sea on some Mediterranean island after dark. One of your friends puts down their drink and mentions that the stars look so much brighter than at home. You all gaze skyward just as a particle the size of a grain of sand smashes into Earth's atmosphere, leaving a bright trail across the night sky as it vaporises. There are gasps and wishes are made in honour of witnessing a shooting star.

Actually, a 'shooting star' is just the popular name for this sort of event. Astronomically you'd call it a meteor and each one that occurs has a great tale to tell.

Most meteor-making objects come from comets, which are icy, dusty and dirty chunks that orbit around the Solar System. The parts of a comet's track that are close enough to the Sun warm up and the ice is evaporated away, while any solid bits that were trapped in the ice are released into space.

These small bits of 'dust', known as meteoroids, generally follow the comet, but each particle's orbit can be changed by factors such as the planets and moons, or even sunlight. So basically, these tiny meteoroids can end up anywhere in the Solar System. If Earth happens to be nearby, then the meteoroids are in trouble.

A FLAMING ENTRANCE

There's a general belief that a shooting star is caused by a meteoroid travelling fast and hitting Earth's atmosphere. But we shouldn't discount the tremendous speed at which Earth moves through space. Our planet's average orbital speed is 30km/s, which is an incredible 108,000km/h (67,000mph). If you're a meteoroid hurtling through space and along comes a whopping planet that hits you at a speed like this, then there are going to be consequences.

These consequences are a fine example of how the atmosphere protects us from space debris such as meteoroids. As the sand grain-sized particle enters the atmosphere, the friction generated by passing through the gases causes it to heat up to the point where vaporisation occurs. The energy

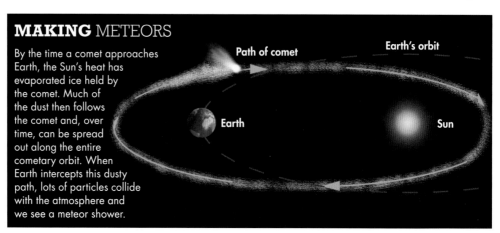

MAKING METEORS

By the time a comet approaches Earth, the Sun's heat has evaporated ice held by the comet. Much of the dust then follows the comet and, over time, can be spread out along the entire cometary orbit. When Earth intercepts this dusty path, lots of particles collide with the atmosphere and we see a meteor shower.

Path of comet

Earth's orbit

Earth

Sun

THE PERSEIDS

One of the best meteor showers of the year, the Perseids, takes place in August. Its high ZHR of 80 meteors per hour, together with the warm summer nights, make it ideal for observing. The peak of the shower occurs around 12 August, but as Perseid activity lasts from mid July until mid August, you have plenty of opportunities to see them.

LOOKING TOWARDS NORTHEAST

Look northeast below Cassiopeia to see the Perseids in all their glory

METEOR DIARY

QUADRANTIDS
Peak around 3 January with a maximum of 120 meteors per hour. The shower is active in early January.

ETA AQUARIDS
Peak around 6 May with a maximum of 60 meteors per hour. The shower is active in early May.

ORIONIDS
Peak around 21 October with a maximum of 26 meteors per hour. The shower is active in mid to late October.

LEONIDS
Peak around 18 November with a maximum of 15 (could be higher) meteors per hour. The shower is active in mid to late November.

GEMINIDS
Peak on 13 December with a maximum of 110 meteors per hour. The shower is active in mid to late December.

produced during this process is displayed as a glowing trail of ionised gas. In other words, when you see a shooting star, it's not the falling object that's engulfed in flames, it's the energetic gases around the vaporising particle that you can see as a white-hot trail.

On average, you can see around five shooting stars per hour on any night, but August sees the return of the annual Perseids meteor shower, with a zenithal hourly rate (ZHR) of 80. The ZHR is the number of meteors seen an hour under perfect conditions, with the shower radiant (the point from which the meteors emanate) directly overhead. If you want to become an expert meteor spotter, this is a great time to get started.

METEORITE OR METEOROID?

A Meteoroid is a small object orbiting out in space, with the potential to meet Earth. Meteoroids are the debris from comets or asteroids.

A Meteor, commonly known as a shooting star, is a bright streak of light seen in the daytime or night sky, caused by a meteoroid entering the atmosphere.

A Meteorite is the surviving part of a meteoroid that was large enough not to get completely burnt up before it hit the ground.

At 60 tonnes, the Hoba meteorite in Namibia is the largest known on Earth

LOOK OUT! METEORITES

SOME OF THESE CHUNKS OF SPACE ROCK LEAVE KILOMETRE-WIDE CRATERS, WHILE OTHERS ALLOW US TO TOUCH OTHER WORLDS

Right now, out there in the Solar System, millions of tiny bits of rock are flying around. They all go unnoticed, until our planet gets in their path. These particles, which can be as small as a grain of sand, travel at such a high speed that they burn and glow as they shoot through the upper atmosphere. And if they're large enough, they may even make it down to the ground.

In astro-speak, these bits of rock have three different names depending on where they are. When they're in space they're meteoroids; once they're in the atmosphere and we see them racing across the night sky they become meteors; and if any of them reach the ground without burning up, they are known as meteorites.

At this point it's worth mentioning that we do not get any meteorites from the famous meteor showers that we see each year, such as the Perseids in August, or the Orionids in October. These showers are produced by tiny, dust-like particles that are too small to reach the ground and are left around the Solar System by comets.

Most meteorites, the chunks of rock that reach Earth's surface, come from the asteroid belt, the area of the Solar System between the orbits of Mars and Jupiter where there are thousands of large rocky objects. These asteroids occasionally hit each other, sending debris flying out into space. It may be millions of years later that one chunk from such an incident, maybe helped by the vast gravity of Jupiter, encounters Earth.

They are not all made of the same stuff: 94 per cent are stony, about five per cent are a mix of stone and iron, while just one per cent are pure

COLLECTING METEORITES

If you think about it, meteorites are the only substantial things not originating from Earth that you can collect. For as little as £5 a gram you can get your hands on something that may have originated far out in space in the asteroid belt. Of course, for this amount of money, your meteorites will be small, and getting hold of a fragment of a meteorite from Mars or the Moon will be much more expensive – we're talking hundreds of pounds a gram. There are plenty of sites on the internet where you can buy meteorites: try starting a search at www.spacerocksuk.com or www.aerolite.org.

Discovered in Namibia in 1838, a fragment of the Gibeon meteorite costs £2 a gram

iron. From this, you would think that most of the 20,000 or so meteorites found so far on Earth are stony. In fact, because stony meteorites crumble away more easily in the atmosphere and look remarkably like ordinary stones, the majority of collected meteorites are stony-iron and iron types; their markings and colour make them stand out from their surroundings.

There are places in the world where any meteorites, regardless of type, will instantly be identified – areas such as the Sahara and Atacama deserts and the Antarctic snowfields. Several rocks from Mars and the Moon have been found in Antarctica, which goes to show that meteorite-delivering collisions can happen anywhere in the Solar System and not just in the asteroid belt.

DEEP IMPACT

Of course, Earth has encountered things much larger than small rocks over its lifetime – meteorites that are never found, but which have certainly left their mark. Big rocks, measuring tens of metres across and weighing more than 1,000 tonnes, aren't slowed down or burnt up in the atmosphere, unlike their much smaller cousins. As a result, these falling rocks end up smashing into Earth's surface with colossal force; the average speed of a body entering our atmosphere is about 20km/s (45,000mph).

The Chicxulub Crater in Mexico is the site of a 180km (112 mile) wide crater created when an object about 10km (6 miles) in diameter hit Earth roughly 65 million years ago, maybe contributing to the demise of the dinosaurs. An easier to view, smaller example is the famous Barringer Crater near Flagstaff in Arizona, which is over 1km across and 170m deep. It was made about 50,000 years ago by an object 50m in diameter. When will the next big one hit? Only time will tell.

ROCKS THAT FELL FROM SPACE

THE CARANCAS METEORITE

Peru, 15 September 2007
After streaking through the sky just before midday, the flaming rock hit Earth with a massive explosion that broke windows over a kilometre away. The resulting crater was about 13m across and 4.5m deep. Locals who flocked to the impact site saw boiling water in the crater and gases billowing out. Later, many of them fell sick. Studies revealed it was due to inhaling the gases from the crater. It turned out not to be a space virus, but a sulphur compound in the rock that was released by the impact.

The 13m x 4.5m impact crater near the village of Carancas in Peru

THE BUZZARD COULEE METEORITE

Canada, 20 November 2008
Thousands saw this rock, estimated to weigh 10 tonnes, as it flamed through the sky. It was certainly disintegrating as, to date, no impact crater has been found, although many meteorites from the broken-up parent were spread over a large area. Space-rock hunters converged on the expected area and it wasn't long before meteorites were located. Large chunks have already been found, one weighing 13kg. Current estimates are that there are possibly tens of thousands of meteorites from this event waiting to be discovered.

This 13kg rock is the largest piece of the Buzzard Coulee meteorite found so far

SATELLITES

THEY FLOAT FAR ABOVE OUR HEADS, HELPING US TO COMMUNICATE AND NAVIGATE, BUT YOU CAN SEE SATELITES WITH YOUR NAKED EYE

The International Space Station is as bright as Venus in the night sky

Who would have thought that a silver ball could change the world? That's what Sputnik 1 did on 4 October 1957. Not only did it start the Space Race between the former USSR and the USA, which led to man walking on the Moon, but it also paved the way for the technological advances that we take for granted today.

The advances that led to accurate weather forecasts, which can predict the course of a hurricane, and the global positioning system (GPS), used to pinpoint those in danger, all owe a great debt to the technology that followed Sputnik 1 into orbit around our planet.

Sputnik orbited for three months before re-entering Earth's atmosphere and burning up. In its wake the number of satellites sent up grew. Today thare are around 900 active satellites circling Earth. Some peer out into space making astronomical observations, while others study

SATELLITES YOU CAN SEE

INTERNATIONAL SPACE STATION
Speed: 7.7km/s
Height: 340km
Now that the Space Station is nearly complete, the reflection from its huge solar arrays is very bright. It can shine as brilliantly as Venus – that's around mag. –4.0, and is an unmistakable sight if you are looking roughly in the right direction. It takes three or four minutes to pass overhead.

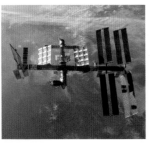

HUBBLE SPACE TELESCOPE
Speed: 7.5km/s
Height: 590km
This magnificent orbiting observatory got a refit in 2009 from the Shuttle, extending the life of this satellite that has provided us with some of the most stunning views of the heavens. It appears as a faint moving dot shining at only mag +3.0, so your observing site needs to be free of light pollution to see it.

IRIDIUM SATELLITES
Speed: 7.4km/s
Height: 780km
There are 66 of these satellites. They form a communications network that makes it possible to speak to someone anywhere in the world via hand-held satellite phones. From Earth, they appear as the brightest satellites. They can shine at mag –9.0 as the solar panels reflect the Sun's light. This is called a satellite flare.

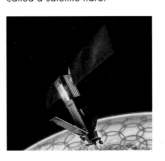

ENVISAT
Speed: 7.4km/s
Height: 790km
This huge environmental satellite built by the European Space Agency has been in orbit since 2002. To date, it is the largest Earth observation spacecraft ever built but its mission came to a premature end in 2012. From a dark location you can still see it in orbit, however, shining with a magnitude of just +3.5.

Earth's environment, tracking things such as global warming, and yet more help us communicate around the world.

Don't forget that the word 'satellite' can include craft big enough for people to climb into. So the International Space Station (ISS) is a satellite, and even the Space Shuttle was classed as a satellite while it was in orbit.

The Space Shuttle was retired in 2011, but when it was in service, it had another thing in common with the ISS. Both would orbit quite close to Earth for a satellite – just 340km (180 miles) from the surface of our planet. At that range, a satellite is in what's called low Earth orbit (LEO), which goes from 160km (100 miles) to 2,000km (1,200 miles) up. You'll find most satellites in LEO because it's comparatively cheap to put them there and you get good views of Earth. At this range, satellites travel around 8km/s (18,000mph) and zip round the planet in about 90 minutes.

THE DEPTHS OF SPACE

The farthest away a satellite can orbit stretches to tens of thousands of kilometres. How high you position one depends on what it's going to do and how much money you have – the farther from Earth, the more expensive it is. After LEO is medium Earth orbit (MEO), which stretches from 2,000km (1,200 miles) out to just below 35,786km (22,000 miles). If you have a GPS unit, then it will be picking up signals from a GPS satellite in MEO travelling at speeds of 3.9km/s (9,000mph), taking almost 12 hours to make one orbit of Earth.

The outer edge of MEO marks the start of geosynchronous orbit. This is where a satellite is placed in order to orbit at the same speed that Earth rotates, so it remains over one spot on the surface. If you have a satellite dish on your house it will be pointing to one of these satellites.

Beyond that is high Earth orbit (HEO). This is used for satellites with a highly elliptical orbit, where their furthest distance is beyond geosynchronous orbit. Here you'll find some communication satellites and a few used for spying, travelling along their orbits between 2-10km/s (4,000-22,000mph) depending on their distance to Earth.

So what about seeing them? It's quite amazing, given the relatively small size of satellites, how many of them you can see in LEO on a clear dark night with just your eyes. The Heavens Above website (www.heavens-above.com) will help you locate any that are flying over your home. You just enter the details of where you live and up pops a list explaining when and where to look for any satellites around, and also how bright they will appear. So, why not get out and see if you can identify a satellite tonight?

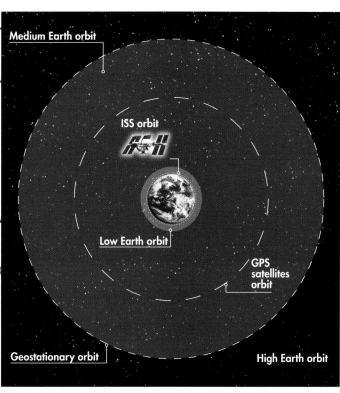

Sputnik 1, the first satellite in space

There are three distinct regions where a satellite can go into orbit around the Earth. The ISS is close to home in Low Earth Orbit (LEO)

SPACE JUNK

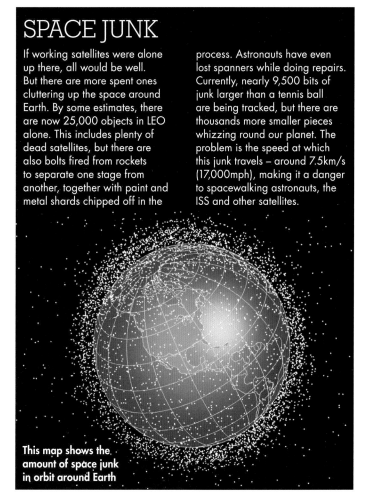

If working satellites were alone up there, all would be well. But there are more spent ones cluttering up the space around Earth. By some estimates, there are now 25,000 objects in LEO alone. This includes plenty of dead satellites, but there are also bolts fired from rockets to separate one stage from another, together with paint and metal shards chipped off in the process. Astronauts have even lost spanners while doing repairs. Currently, nearly 9,500 bits of junk larger than a tennis ball are being tracked, but there are thousands more smaller pieces whizzing round our planet. The problem is the speed at which this junk travels – around 7.5km/s (17,000mph), making it a danger to spacewalking astronauts, the ISS and other satellites.

This map shows the amount of space junk in orbit around Earth

An aurora is an amazing natural phenomenon caused by the solar wind and Earth's magnetosphere

AMAZING AURORAE

DISCOVER HOW THESE BEAUTIFUL CURTAINS OF LIGHT ARE FORMED

Above the northern horizon a green arc melts into view. As you watch, red and green rays begin to emanate from it. These grow into long weaving ripples that stretch like ribbons across the entire sky, almost as if they were blowing in the wind. You are witnessing one of the true marvels of the natural world: an aurora.

The phenomenon is caused by charged particles streaming out of the Sun and interacting with Earth's magnetic field – our planet's protective shield – which channels them down towards the 'magnetic' poles. As the particles reach lower altitudes, usually between 80 and 200km, they hit and excite the the gases in Earth's atmosphere, causing a distinctive and colourful glow.

The magnetic poles are about 11° away from the geographical poles (the ones traditionally refered to as the North and South Poles). So you stand a

much better chance of seeing all this activity in far northern or southern latitudes.

Earth's magnetic field is similar to the field from the north and south poles of a bar magnet. This means that there will be the same activity at each pole – any aurora happening around the north pole will also be happening almost identically around the south pole.

NORTH VS SOUTH

Aurorae are easier to see in the northern hemisphere, for various reasons. Norway, for example, is inhabited along the coast because of the warm Gulf Stream. This makes it easier to get closer to the action – a cruise can take you into aurora country. In the southern hemisphere, the aurora sits over Antarctica, which is not an easy place to get to. From this frozen continent there is a lot of ocean before you reach landfall in New Zealand or southern Chile for instance, where you have a smaller chance of seeing a display.

The word aurora comes from the Roman goddess of dawn. In mythology she flies around in the mornings announcing the arrival of the Sun. Knowing the word's origin enables us to appreciate the names given to these phenomena. At the North Pole is the Aurora Borealis, which translates as the Northern Dawn, while its counterpart at the South Pole is referred to as the Aurora Australis, or Southern Dawn.

Thankfully, aurorae are not always confined to high latitudes, and this is where the activity of the Sun comes into play. An active Sun has more sunspots, but it also sends more particles streaming out, which leads to more auroral activity on Earth in terms of frequency and magnitude. The most massive Sun-particle storms can even cause aurorae to be seen at the equator. While these are extremely rare, you can certainly see a couple of aurorae each year from Scotland and northern England.

Unfortunately, the Sun won't get noticeably more active for another two or three years, but there's still bound to be the odd display visible from the north of the UK. So make sure you keep an eye out for signs of the wonderful aurora.

AURORAE ON OTHER PLANETS

Aurorae aren't only confined to Earth. They have been seen on many other Solar System worlds too. Jupiter and Saturn both have magnetic fields much stronger than Earth's, and so it isn't surprising to find some amazing aurorae around their north and south magnetic poles.

In addition, activity has also been seen around some of Jupiter's largest moons, such as Europa and Io. Aurorae have also been seen on Uranus and Neptune, and to a much lesser extent around Mars, where there are only small regions of magnetic field.

Hubble reveals a strong auroral display at Saturn's poles

Jupiter exhibits aurorae in these images from Hubble

WHEN EARTH MEETS THE SUN

The magnetosphere is the area of influence that Earth's magnetic field has in space. It protects life on our planet from all sorts of radiation that would otherwise penetrate into the atmosphere and reach the ground.

The Sun releases vast amounts of charged particles called the solar wind that fly in all directions through space. Being so close to the Sun, Earth gets a fair blast of this and so

we rely on our magnetic field to deflect the particles that constantly flow through our part of space.

The shape of the magnetosphere is a result of how the magnetic influences of the Earth and Sun interact. On the Sun side it is pushed towards Earth and the boundary is known as the bow shock. On Earth's far side, the magnetosphere trails, looking

similar to the wake behind a rock in a flowing river; this is called the magnetotail.

When the solar wind is particularly strong, Earth's magnetic field gets overloaded, and the extra particles follow the magnetic field lines that cascade down into the atmosphere towards the North and South Poles, giving rise to the marvellous aurorae.

Magnetosphere boundary

Bow shock

SOLAR WIND

Sun

Magnetosphere

Aurorae

Magnetotail

Diagram not to scale

Charged particles from the Sun are channelled to the poles by Earth's magnetosphere

WHAT CAUSES THE AURORA?

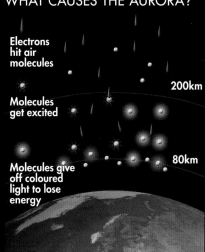

Electrons hit air molecules

200km

Molecules get excited

Molecules give off coloured light to lose energy

80km

Solar wind electrons hit atmospheric particles

JACK FINCH/SCIENCE PHOTO LIBRARY, JPL/NASA/STSCI X 2, ILLUSTRATIONS BY PAUL WOOTTON

Outer Arm

Core

Sagittarius-Carina Arm

Norma Arm

Scutum-Crux Arm

Perseus Arm

Orion-Cygnus Arm

Solar System

THE MILKY WAY

DISCOVER THE HUGE ISLAND OF STARS THAT IS OUR HOME GALAXY

MARK GARLICK/SCIENCE PHOTO LIBRARY X 2, PETE LAWRENCE

Our Galaxy, the Milky Way, is one of the most magical sights of the night. Away from light-polluted regions our Galaxy looks like a river of light. It becomes clearly visible every year as autumn approaches, the brightest part of it adorning our skies.

The term Milky Way can refer to several different objects, as well as a famous chocolate bar. Some use it to refer to the weaving band of light crossing the sky,

created by the hundreds of thousands of faint, distant stars whose light combines to form this wonderful feature.

However, there's much more to our Galaxy than these stars, which are just the visible part of it. The term Milky Way is also used to describe our entire Galaxy, a huge island of stars of which our Sun is a member, and not just the band of light we see. If we were to look down at our Galaxy from

afar, as shown in the image above, the view would look much like a spinning Catherine Wheel firework. This particular 'firework' is made up of somewhere between 200 and 400 billion stars, and is believed to be around 3.2 billion years old. From its bright, bulging centre emanate several arms, which spiral outwards.

A closer look reveals that these spiral arms come out of the ends of a bar that runs

through the central bulge. This means that the Milky Way is a member of the class of galaxies known as barred spirals.

The arms form what's known as the galactic disc, where the majority of stars live, including the Sun. And because of all the dust and gas that floats about there, the arms are also where new stars are being born. Beyond that, outside the main disc, there's a halo that surrounds the Milky

Our Solar System sits in one of the many spiral arms, away from the core

OUR VIEW OF THE GALAXY

From Earth we see the stars of our Galaxy in a band all around us because of our position within the disc of the Milky Way. However, they're not evenly spread around the sky. If you look in the direction of the constellations Orion and Monoceros, you are basically looking out of the main disc into deep space. There are fewer stars there and so the Milky Way is less noticeable. Look in the opposite direction, towards Sagittarius and Scorpius, and you're looking directly into the heart of our Galaxy. Here there's much more dust, gas and stars. The Milky Way is visible all year round, but it's higher in the sky in April and September.

The brightest part of the Milky Way can be seen in the constellation of Sagittarius

Way containing hundreds of huge, spherical groups of stars known as globular clusters.

Needless to say, all of this is big. Very big. Our Galaxy has a diameter of around 100,000 lightyears, while the spiral arms have a thickness of between 1,000 and 2,000 lightyears. A lightyear is the distance that light can travel in one year.

Our star, the Sun, sits about 25,000 lightyears from the centre, on the edge of what is known as the Orion-Cygnus, or Local, Arm. This is a minor spiral arm of the Galaxy that sits between the major Sagittarius-Carina Arm inside it and the Perseus Arm on the outside.

TELESCOPE TRIUMPH

So how do we know all of this? Well, as soon as telescopes were powerful enough to make out the spirals of other galaxies, we began piecing together the similarities between those that were far off and our own. And once astronomers were able to peer into the skies with radio and infrared telescopes, they were able to see through the dust and gas that stops observations of visible light – and saw the stars in the galactic arms beyond.

We certainly don't know everything yet, but advances in technology in the years to come are likely to reveal much more about our Galaxy. We may even find out where the mysterious substance known as dark matter is located. Among other things, it is thought to have an influence on how the entire Galaxy rotates.

MEET THE NEIGHBOURS

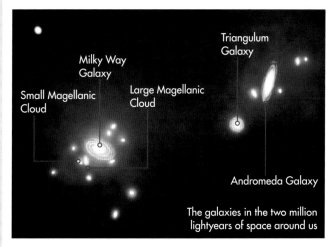

The galaxies in the two million lightyears of space around us

The Milky Way isn't alone in our part of the Universe. Beyond the clusters of stars that form a halo around us, we have a number of neighbours. Together these are part of what's called the Local Group. This is a family of about 30 big and small galaxies sitting in an area of space around 10 million lightyears in diameter.

We are in one of the big three galaxies within the group. The other two are the Andromeda and Triangulum Galaxies. The rest are fairly small dwarf-type galaxies, some of which are satellites of the big three. For example, the most famous satellite galaxies of the Milky Way are the Large and Small Magellanic Clouds. These can only be seen from the southern hemisphere and look like round pieces of the Milky Way that have broken off.

According to the latest research, our Galaxy and the Andromeda Galaxy are approaching each other and will collide in around five billion years' time. The Sun's death throes would have made the Earth uninhabitable by then, so there's no need to worry about the consequences of a collision.

OBSERVING THE MILKY WAY

WHEN THE NIGHTS DRAW IN AND DARKER SKIES BECOME THE NORM, TAKE THE OPPORTUNITY TO VIEW THE MILKY WAY IN ALL ITS GLORY

Our position inside the Galaxy allows us to see the stars that make up the other arms of the Milky Way as a band arcing across the heavens. But since we're well away from the centre of the Galaxy, the arc isn't evenly spread around the sky. If we look in the direction of the constellations of Orion and Monoceros, we are looking out of our Galaxy's plane into empty space. This means that in the UK the dark nights of late winter and early spring are not the best time to see the Milky Way.

However, in the opposite direction, towards Sagittarius and Scorpius, we are looking directly into the teeming centre of our Galaxy. More dust, more gas and more stars create a river of light here, making it bigger and brighter. Autumn evenings are the best time to view this celestial stream.

The river of light that is the Milky Way and, inset, an artist's impression of the Sun's place in the Galaxy

Location of the Sun

GALAXY TOURS

👁 WITH THE NAKED EYE

THE GALACTIC ARC

Best seen: Autumn
Even though the Milky Way can be seen from mildly light-polluted areas, it will only be visible as a brighter wash across the night sky. To truly view its amazing structure and detail in high contrast, look at it from a really dark location.

SAGITTARIUS

Best seen: August and September
It may be quite low on the horizon from the UK, but if you can find a reasonably dark location this constellation can still reveal our Galaxy at its brightest and best, since we're looking right into its central area.

CYGNUS

Best seen: September to November
A section of the Milky Way runs the length of this constellation. Here you'll see the dust and gas within our Galaxy obscuring the bright stars beyond. There's much to look out for – dark rifts and brighter patches galore.

PERSEUS AND CASSIOPEIA

Best seen: September and October
Another fine, diverse area of the Milky Way, made more glorious by the bright Double Cluster in Perseus. You can't ask for much more than these two glorious concentrations of stars, which are both visible to the naked eye.

🔭 WITH BINOCULARS

DOUBLE CLUSTER IN PERSEUS

Best seen: October to February
These two Galactic star clusters form a perfectly sized object for binocular viewing, and what targets they are: two concentrated clumps of stars sitting within the melee of Galactic star clouds that surround it.

M8, THE LAGOON NEBULA

Best seen: July and August
This easily noticeable accumulation of dust and gas can be seen as a brighter patch in 10x50 binoculars, even sitting where it does within the constellation of Sagittarius – a busy and star-rich area of the Milky Way.

M35, OPEN CLUSTER

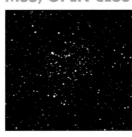

Best seen: January to March
This star cluster in Gemini can just about be seen with the naked eye under clear skies. It's a very good target for binoculars, which should reveal about a dozen out of the 200 or so stars in its elongated shape.

NGC 7000, THE NA NEBULA

Best seen: September to December
It takes a bit of practice to see NGC 7000, also known as the North America Nebula, as it's such a large object. The surrounding area in Cygnus has so many features for binoculars, like open cluster M39, that it's worth the effort.

🔭 WITH A SMALL TELESCOPE

M27, DUMBBELL NEBULA

Best seen: September to November
This wonderful planetary nebula in the constellation of Vulpecula is well worth a look. It appears as a misty oval. Nearby stars and the marvellous backdrop of the Milky Way complete the view.

ALBIREO, BETA CYGNI

Best seen: September to November
It would be hard to find a better double star in the sky. Golden Albireo A and blue Albireo B sit in a field of faint stars. The two components are easily separated with a small telescope.

M17, THE OMEGA NEBULA

Best seen: August and September
This glowing nebula sits among the star fields of the constellation of Sagittarius. It has a curved shape that can be likened to the Greek capital letter omega, Ω, hence its name. It's sometimes called the Swan Nebula.

M16, THE EAGLE NEBULA

Best seen: August and September
This cluster of around 100 stars in the constellation of Serpens is embedded in a fine cloud of gas, the Eagle Nebula, which features in one of the Hubble Space Telescope's most iconic images – the 'Pillars of Creation'.

DEEP SKY
NEBULAE

NEBULAE COME IN A PLETHORA OF SHAPES AND SIZES, AND ARE AMONG THE MOST DIVERSE AND BEAUTIFUL DEEP-SKY OBJECTS YOU CAN SEE

Before the dawn of the telescope, only exceptionally bright objects were visible to those looking skywards. They only hinted at the wide variety of different objects lurking in the depths of our Universe: the so-called deep-sky objects.

In the old days they all went by the Latin name of nebulae, or 'little mists' in English, simply because they all looked like small, light, fuzzy, foggy patches in the otherwise black night. Once telescopes became more powerful, it became clear that not all nebulae were the same. Astronomers became aware that there were objects as varied as galaxies, globular clusters and supernova remnants.

The term 'nebula' became narrower, being used to describe deep-sky objects made up of huge clouds of dust and gas

The Horsehead Nebula is a great example of a dark nebula

many lightyears across. This doesn't make nebulae any less interesting though, because they still include many of the most visually stunning things in deep space. Their colours can be revealed by a good camera attached to a telescope. They're also the result and cause of some of the most exciting activity in the Universe: star death and star birth.

Nebulae are divided into different classifications, and every one of them lets us know what is going on in the cloud or how it was formed. These include general emission, reflection and dark nebulae, as well as planetary and supernova remnants. Each has a story to tell.

Emission nebula, like the Orion Nebula, are the birthplace of stars. Radiation

from the newborn stars created in the nebula causes the cloud of gas and dust to glow, and this lets us see it. The nebula itself is actually giving out light, hence its name.

LIT BY THE STARS

Reflection nebulae, like the one around the Pleiades star cluster, are only visible because there are some stars nearby that light up the gas and dust, just as the Sun lights up a cloud in an otherwise blue sky.

Dark nebulae, such as the Horsehead Nebula, are dark dust clouds. They are only visible because they are in front of a bright nebula or field of stars. We effectively see a silhouette of the cloud, but no detail in it.

You might think that planetary nebulae, such as the Ring Nebula, have something to do with planets, but you'd be wrong. They get their name

THE STELLAR NURSERY

1 Nebulae are where stars are created. One idea of how it all starts is that a shock wave from a nearby supernova explosion compresses the cloud. Once the density of the gas passes a critical point, gravity takes over.

2 Gravity causes clumps of the nebula to pull together. The pressure at the centre of the clumps builds and the temperature rises dramatically. If there is enough gas to fuel the process, the region can become a protostar.

3 If the temperature in the clump reaches 10 million °C, the nuclear furnace that powers stars ignites. Over tens of millions of years it settles into normal life and joins what's called the main sequence, like our own Sun.

T.A RECTOR (NOAO/AURA/NSF) AND HUBBLE HERITAGE TEAM (STSCI/AURA/NASA), N. SMITH (UNIVERSITY OF CALIFORNIA, BERKELEY) AND NOAO/AURA/NSF, NASA/ESA/J. HESTER AND A. LOLL (ARIZONA STATE UNIVERSITY), PAUL WOOTTON, WILL GATER

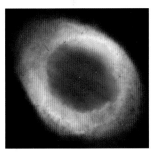

Clockwise from this image: The Carina Nebula, a stunning emission nebula; the Pleiades star cluster is given a ghostly hue by a reflection nebula; the Crab Nebula is a dramatic supernova remnant; the Ring Nebula, a planetary nebula

because, through a telescope, many have the appearance of a faint, small, fuzzy disc and look a lot like a planet. These nebulae are formed during the death of a star of similar mass to the Sun. As it grows unstable, the star puffs off its gaseous atmosphere to form clouds around it. Stars larger than the Sun end their days explosively in a supernova, leaving a spectacular remnant in their wake.

You'll find details of where to locate nebulae from the many catalogues that have been made by astronomers. One of the most famous lists was made by the 18th-century observer Charles Messier. His catalogue of 110 objects includes 12 nebulae. Many star atlases include the Messier Catalogue. See if yours does – you may be able to spot a nebula tonight.

THE ORION NEBULA

One of the most famous deep-space objects visible with the naked eye

Out of all the types of nebula, the only one that can be easily seen with the naked eye is the Orion Nebula, M42. Not surprisingly, it's the brightest nebula in the night sky, and that makes it perfect for practising on.

With a casual glance below the three belt stars of Orion in a dark, light-pollution free sky, you'll see it as a small misty smudge. A pair of binoculars will begin to reveal its curving shape. With a small telescope, you will start to see some structure in this vast cloud 1,600 lightyears away.

In the heart of the Orion Nebula you'll see four stars. These are part of the Trapezium open cluster, named because of the shape the four stars form. It's the radiation from these stars that is energising the entire nebula and causing it to glow.

A spectacular treat through a small telescope: the Orion Nebula

A representation of the blast that formed the Crab Nebula, which can be seen in image 6

1

2

3

DEEP SKY SUPERNOVAE

DISCOVER ONE OF THE MOST FEROCIOUS EVENTS IN THE UNIVERSE: A STAR'S DEATH

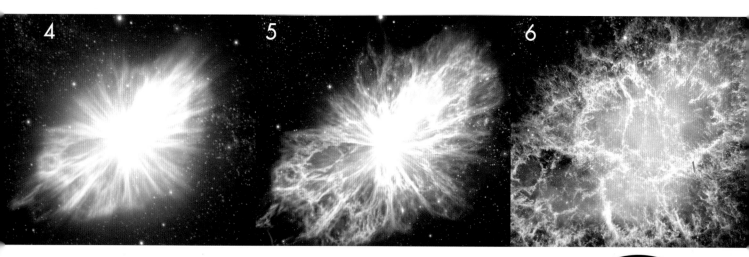

4

5

6

Stars are seemingly steady, inactive things in the night sky. They shine away, puncturing the blackness of the night like silent, benign candles. In reality, each and every one is an amazingly extreme object. A star lives its life ferociously, creating energy to hold itself in balance against the phenomenal force of gravity acting upon it.

For most stars this works tremendously well – until the fuel runs out. For massive stars that are nine to 10 times the size of the Sun, the end is inevitable: it comes as a supernova, a cataclysmic explosion in which most of

FAMOUS SUPERNOVAE

Astronomers expect a supernova to occur in our Galaxy once every 50 years. Unfortunately, not all are visible to us because some are hidden by the vast dust clouds in the Milky Way.

In fact, the last supernova that was actually observed in our Galaxy was back in October 1604. It was written about and subsequently named after the German mathematician and astronomer Johannes Kepler. This was the second supernova to be observed in that generation; only 32 years earlier, in 1572, the Danish astronomer Tycho Brahe, one of the last great, pre-telescope observers, made detailed notes on another. It was named Tycho's Supernova after him.

Much brighter than both of those – in fact brilliant enough to be clearly seen in daytime for 23 days – was the supernova that caused the Crab Nebula. This was observed in 1054 by Chinese, Arabic and Japanese astronomers. Rock art indicates that native American tribes may have seen the event too.

Back to the present day and as of April 2009, the uninspiringly named G1.9+0.3, inset, holds the record for the youngest known supernova remnant in our Galaxy. It exploded around 25,000 years ago, but its light only started to reach us 140 years ago.

As it explodes, Supernova 1987a, bottom right, rivals the brightness of the Tarantula Nebula, top left

REMARKABLE
REMNANTS

When massive stars explode, they throw off their outer layers at blistering speeds. The rapidly expanding shells of gas and dust create spectacular objects known as supernova remnants. These stellar carcasses are some of the most intricate deep-sky objects. Their beauty has been captured with the help of space telescopes observing at many wavelengths of light, as shown below.

CRAB NEBULA
First observed by the English astronomer John Bevis in 1731, this famous remnant is the first object in the Messier Catalogue. The 1054 supernova that caused it was so bright that it was visible during the daytime.
Constellation: Taurus
Distance: 6,250 lightyears

VEIL NEBULA
The explosion that created this relatively large remnant occurred almost 10,000 years ago. It was discovered by German-born English astronomer William Herschel in 1784.
Constellation: Cygnus
Distance: 2,000 lightyears

3C 10
In November 1572 the supernova that created 3C 10 was observed by Danish astronomer Tycho Brahe. This spectacular ball is also known as Tycho's Supernova Remnant.
Constellation: Cassiopeia
Distance: 7,500 lightyears

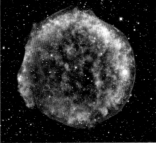

KEPLER'S SUPERNOVA
The last supernova observed in our Galaxy. Spotted in 1604 by Johannes Kepler, it left an amazing remnant of colourful gas and dust.
Constellation: Ophiuchus
Distance: 20,000 lightyears

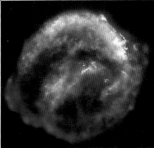

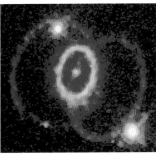

SN 1987A
This distant supernova was spotted in 1987 in the Large Magellanic Cloud, a dwarf galaxy near the Milky Way. This Hubble Space Telescope image of the remnant shows several looping rings of material.
Constellation: Dorado
Distance: 168,000 lightyears

the star's matter is blasted out into space, with a vast increase in brightness that can last from weeks to months.

The exact story of a supernova involves several stages. A massive star will live for millions of years, happily converting its main fuel of hydrogen into helium, until the hydrogen runs low. With enough mass, the temperature and pressure in its core are high enough for helium to be used as fuel, and the outer layer of the star gets pushed away from the core. Eventually the helium runs low and more changes happen: other elements are created through nuclear reactions and then used as fuel. All the time the star is growing larger, becoming a red supergiant.

TIME BOMB

If the star is massive enough, an iron core eventually forms. The star will not create any elements heavier than this within its core. This heavy, very dense core then shuts down and collapses under gravity.

With no internal pressure holding it up, the rest of the star's matter also falls inwards. It hits the core and rebounds back into space at a speed of 70 million km/h, in an explosion that generates a vast amount of energy.

Even though these supernovae are often bright enough to outshine entire galaxies, only a tiny fraction of the energy released is visible light. Most of the energy is released in the form of subatomic particles. When the drama is over, what remains is the old, dead core of the star radiating away its heat. It's now a compact neutron star or, if the star is more massive, a black hole.

This is what happens with a typical supernova, which astronomers call a Type II supernova. There are also Type Ia, Ib and Ic supernovae, of which Type Ia are the most interesting. This is where an old star, much like the Sun, has already died and become a white dwarf star, but is pulling gas off a nearby star. When the white dwarf has built up enough mass, nuclear reactions can take place and a supernova can erupt.

Type Ia supernovae are useful as they all explode with pretty much the same brightness as each other, so they can be used to measure distances from the Earth. It's also worth noting that during a Type II supernova, material like carbon and oxygen is thrown out. In fact, all the elements we are made from and rely on come from these final moments of a dying star.

DEEP SKY
GALAXIES AND CLUSTERS

THE UNIVERSE IS FULL OF STARS THAT GROUP TOGETHER INTO CLUSTERS LARGE AND SMALL, AND VAST COLLECTIONS CALLED GALAXIES, WHICH COME IN ALL MANNER OF GUISES

New stars form within the hazy confines of emission nebulae. Over an incredibly long time, all of an emission nebula's gas is either pulled into new stars or pushed away into space by their radiation, revealing a new stellar family – an open star cluster.

How many stars there are in an open cluster depends on the amount of gas and dust in the original nebula. The oft-mentioned Orion Nebula is a great example of an emission nebula that will produce a massive open star cluster in the future, possibly containing around 1,000 stars. Some star clusters are much smaller, containing only a few dozen members.

You can see some pretty fine open clusters using only your eyes, such as the famous Pleiades – also known as the Seven Sisters – and the Hyades, both in the constellation of Taurus, the Bull. We know that these and other open star clusters are families due to the similar make-up of the stars and because they move through space together.

Although hundreds of star clusters are visible through a small telescope, the brightness of these two is due to their relative closeness to Earth. The Pleiades is 380 lightyears away, while the Hyades is only 150 lightyears away.

One thing the stars in open clusters do as they age is drift apart. This means that younger clusters are a more tightly knit community. Taking our two friends in Taurus as an example, the compact Pleiades is around 100 million years old, but the looser Hyades has been around for about 790 million years.

GREAT GLOBULARS

Now, just to make things more interesting, there's another sort of star cluster known as a globular. They have nothing to do with open clusters; the only similarity is that both kinds of cluster are made of stars. Globular star clusters are spherical in shape and consist of hundreds of thousands of stars at least – indeed some have several million members.

Unlike young open clusters, which sit within the main body of the Milky Way Galaxy, these ancient globular clusters live in a halo around it and are tens of thousands of lightyears away from us.

We know our Galaxy is surrounded by around 160 globular clusters. You can spot a few with the naked eye, like M13 in the constellation of Hercules, but they are best seen through binoculars or a small telescope.

GALACTIC VARIETY

There are estimated to be 100 billion galaxies in our Universe – these are the main types

SPIRAL
These galaxies take the shape of a flattish disc with a central bulge. The disc itself is made of curving arms of dust, gas and stars that sweep out from the centre.

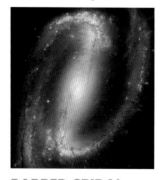

BARRED SPIRAL
These are similar to spiral galaxies, except the arms start from a bar-like structure that stretches out from the centre. Astronomers believe the Milky Way is this type of galaxy.

ELLIPTICAL
The elliptical class may include the largest of all galaxies, but they are rather structureless collections of old stars. They typically have a lot of globular clusters in their outer regions.

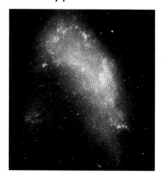

IRREGULAR
Irregular galaxies don't fit into any particular class. A galaxy of this type has probably been involved in a collision with another galaxy, which has twisted its appearance.

NGC 1672 in Dorado is a stunning barred spiral galaxy

The last of our deep-sky objects are galaxies. These appear in a variety of shapes and sizes – see 'Galactic variety' on the left.

GIANT GALAXIES

Occasionally, galaxies are found alone, but most live in small groups, larger clusters or superclusters containing thousands of galaxies, bound together by gravity.

Galaxies are huge objects. The Milky Way is over 100,000 lightyears in diameter and contains somewhere between 200 billion and 400 billion stars. Others, like Andromeda, the largest member of the Local Group have even more.

It's an understatement to say that there really are an awful lot of stars out there.

CATCHING A CLUSTER

Our top picks. Remember: the lower the magnitude, the brighter the cluster

Name: M3
Constellation: Canes Venatici
Magnitude: +6.2
One of the most glorious globulars in the northern hemisphere, it looks like a hazy star in binoculars.

Name: M4
Constellation: Scorpius
Magnitude: +6.0
This large globular cluster is also one of the closest to us, at about 6,500 lightyears away.

Name: M5
Constellation: Serpens
Magnitude: +5.6
A lovely globular that you may be able to see with the naked eye.

Name: M10
Constellation: Ophiuchus
Magnitude: +6.6
A good target with binoculars, this large globular is 14,000 lightyears away.

Name: M12
Constellation: Ophiuchus
Magnitude: +6.6
In the same constellation as M10, this globular is best seen through a pair of binoculars.

Name: M13
Constellation: Hercules
Magnitude: +5.7
The finest globular cluster in the northern hemisphere, it can rarely be seen without binoculars.

Name: M15
Constellation: Pegasus
Magnitude: +6.2
A lovely object to look at with binoculars, this globular is 33,000 lightyears distant.

Name: M22
Constellation: Sagittarius
Magnitude: +5.1
A good naked-eye target, it appears elongated through binoculars.

Name: M92
Constellation: Hercules
Magnitude: +6.5
A gem in binoculars, this is one of the oldest globular clusters known.

THE MESSIER CATALOGUE

HOW A FRENCHMAN'S 18TH-CENTURY LIST OF NIGHT-SKY OBJECTS BECAME THE DEFINITIVE CATALOGUE FOR AMATEUR ASTRONOMERS

Charles Messier intended his catalogue to be a list of things to avoid

For budding and seasoned stargazers in the northern hemisphere, the Messier Catalogue is the most famous observing list of astronomical deep-sky objects. Within the 110-strong catalogue are examples of every known deep-sky object – a good assortment of galaxies, open and globular star clusters, nebulae and one supernova remnant. This is the famous Crab Nebula in Taurus, which is also the first object in the catalogue. It bears the designation Messier 1, commonly written as M1.

The Messier Catalogue has become so ingrained into astronomical lore that objects are commonly described by their Messier number. So 'M42' is often used in place of, or in addition to, the actual name of this object, which is the Orion Nebula.

The irony of this useful catalogue is that it was never intended to be a list of objects for observers to hunt down with their telescopes: rather, it was a list of objects to avoid. This is because Charles Messier, the French astronomer who created the catalogue, was a comet hunter, and many comets appear as faint, fuzzy blobs in the sky – just as deep-sky objects do. So he assembled these deep-sky objects into a list of 'red herrings', in order to make sure they could be discounted during his cometary searches. He conducted these in his observatory, a wood and glass structure atop a tower in the medieval Hôtel de Cluny in Paris.

GROWING NUMBER

The Messier Catalogue first arrived on the scene in 1771 as a list of 45 objects. Ten years later it had been expanded to 103, with some of the later observations being undertaken by Messier's assistant Pierre Méchain. The catalogue stayed at this size for over 100 years.

There were some interesting developments in the 20th century, as astronomers and historians made seven additions to the list. These were not just arbitrary objects, but ones that Messier and Méchain made observing notes about shortly after the final version of the catalogue was published. So it was only in 1967 when M110, a faint dwarf elliptical

The Crab Nebula is M1, the first object in Messier's catalogue

NASA/ESA J. HESTER AND A. LOLL (ARIZONA STATE UNIVERSITY), WILL GATER X 4, ROB GENDLER/WWW.ROBGENDLERASTROPICS.COM X 4

TOP NAKED-EYE MESSIER OBJECTS

M42

The Orion Nebula is a vast cloud of dust and gas – what's known as an emission nebula. It's easy to spot with just your eyes as a misty patch below the three belt stars in the constellation of Orion.

M45

The Pleiades, also known as the Seven Sisters, is an open star cluster in the constellation of Taurus. Depending on your eyesight and how dark the sky is at your location, you'll be able to see between six and 12 stars.

M13

The hundreds of thousands of stars that make up the Great Globular Cluster in Hercules are just visible to the eye from dark locations. It's one-third of the way south on the line between the stars Eta Herculis and Zeta Herculis.

M31

The Andromeda Galaxy is without doubt the most distant object visible to the naked eye, being about 2.8 million lightyears away. Find it in the constellation of Andromeda as a faint smudge in very dark, Moonless skies.

TOP SMALL-SCOPE MESSIER OBJECTS

M81

Looking at Bode's Galaxy in the constellation of Ursa Major with a 3- to 4-inch scope, you'll see it as the brighter of two fuzzy patches close to each other in the night sky. The second patch is another galaxy, the fainter M82.

M51

The Whirlpool Galaxy in the constellation of Canes Venatici is a face-on spiral galaxy. Small scopes reveal the basic shape and the smaller companion with which it is interacting. Larger instruments reveal more structure.

M3

This globular cluster, also in Canes Venatici, is an easy target for a small telescope. It's one of the largest and brightest globulars in the sky; a small scope will reveal great detail and a compact core.

M57

The Ring Nebula in the constellation of Lyra is a shapely planetary nebula, and one of the easiest of its kind to observe. With a 3- to 4-inch scope it's easily seen as a misty but quite defined oval patch.

---

galaxy in the constellation of Andromeda, made its way into the catalogue as the final officially recognised object.

There are several reasons why Charles Messier's 'list of objects to avoid when looking for comets' has become so readily accepted as targets to seek out with a telescope. One is that it isn't too long: 110 objects makes it a nice, manageable number. So manageable, in fact, that some amateurs like to undertake Messier marathons, where they endeavour to observe all 110 objects in one night.

Another reason is that Messier used a variety of different sized scopes in his comet searches, including a 3.5-inch refractor. The objects in his catalogue don't need massively powerful instruments to be seen: they're within reach of small telescopes. Finally, it's a pretty comprehensive list, encompassing almost all of the wondrous sights that novice stargazers would wish to see, many of them bright objects.

Of course, the Messier Catalogue is not the only list – there are more than 110 objects out in space after all. The New General Catalogue (NGC), for example, lists nearly 8,000 objects, followed by an extension known as the Index Catalogue (IC) that adds more than 5,000 on top. You'll also find that many objects appear in multiple catalogues: M42, the Orion Nebula, is also designated as NGC 1976.

However, the NGC and IC lists are little more than databases of deep-sky objects. They have less appeal for amateur astronomers because many of their entries are too faint to see without a professional telescope.

There is, however, one other list that's worth a mention: Patrick Moore's own compilation, the Caldwell Catalogue. This is, in effect, an extension to the Messier Catalogue. It includes many more bright, deep-sky objects that are perfect for you to train your telescope on from your back garden.

The Andromeda Galaxy is similar in form to the Milky Way, but is thought to hold over twice as many stars

SEE THE ANDROMEDA GALAXY

THE SPIRAL GALAXY THAT'S AS FAR AS YOU CAN SEE IN THE UNIVERSE WITH YOUR EYES ALONE

On so many levels, the Andromeda Galaxy is a marvel. Don't be fooled by its deceptively ordinary designation of 'M31', given to it by Charles Messier in his 1781 catalogue of astronomical objects. The more you delve, the more fascinating Andromeda becomes.

Autumn is the best time of year to see the Andromeda Galaxy: it's at its highest in the south at about 8pm. As soon as it gets dark, you can be sure that M31 will already be pretty high. To your naked eye it will look like a fuzzy patch. From urban locations, the galaxy is equally visible in binoculars, even if you have a fair amount of light pollution. But dark, Moonless skies will give you the best views.

Knowing a bit about this fuzzy patch of stars really starts to bring it to life. Firstly, it's the only major galaxy that you can see without any optical aids. Some claim that M33, the Triangulum Galaxy, can be seen with the eyes alone, but at mag. +6.2 it's so ghostly it's almost not there.

Secondly, the distance to the Andromeda Galaxy defies understanding. In Earth units it's a staggering 23 billion billion km away. Using more standard large-scale space units, it's around 2.5 million lightyears away. In other words, you're looking at the galaxy as it was 2.5 million years ago. When you consider that most of the stars we see are just tens or hundreds of lightyears away, the distance to the Andromeda Galaxy becomes phenomenal. This is about the farthest thing in the Universe that you can see using just your eyes.

Another amazing aspect of the galaxy only becomes apparent when you take a photograph of it: its enormous extent in the sky, spanning then width of six full Moons side-by-side.

With bigger telescopes, you'll see a galaxy with spiral arms that's similar to the Milky Way. The Andromeda Galaxy and our own are the two most massive systems in a Local Group of around 30 galaxies. But while our Galaxy has up to 400 billion stars, Andromeda is thought to contain a trillion. With so many more stars, it could mean that there's more chance of life existing over there, in our similar but larger galactic sibling.

Find the Andromeda Galaxy high in the sky in November

WHAT WILL M31 LOOK LIKE

Under dark, Moon-free skies, your unaided eye should be able to find the Andromeda Galaxy as a faint misty patch a short distance from the band of the Milky Way. The ancient Persians called it a 'little cloud'.

Using binoculars, you'll find the galaxy with little or no difficulty. It will be oval in appearance – although you won't be able to make out any of the individual stars within it.

The Andromeda Galaxy looks great through smaller scopes of, say, 4 inches in diameter. The galaxy appears as a larger, elongated oval shape with a core that shows up as a slightly brighter area – like in this picture.